This manual is dedicated to my former and current students for their inspiring influence on me to create this manual for my future students.

AutoCAD® is a registered trademark of Autodesk, Inc.

LEARNING THE ESSENTIAL CONCEPTS OF ENGINEERING GRAPHICS AND AUTOCAD® 2019

Eighth Edition

Slobodan Urdarevik
Master Faculty Specialist
Western Michigan University

Illustrations

Eric Mamo –   Illustrator and editor

PREFACE

This manual was created as a result of many years of experience teaching Engineering Graphics. Use this manual as a tool to obtain the knowledge needed to become more competitive for a job in the field of Engineering Graphics.

One of the biggest problems most engineering (also science and math) students are facing is visualization. I noticed this problem when I was a student, and since then I started thinking of finding a way that can help students to visualize the object as 3 dimensional based on 2 dimensional drawings. There are many studies done on the visualization problem pointing out that STEM (Science Technology Engineering and Math) students who have a natural ability (they are a minority compared to the total number of STEM students) to see the shape of a part in their mind when shown as 2 dimensional drawing, are more successful than the students lacking that ability. Here I will quote Prof. Bertoline's (Purdue University) opinion who says: *"Spatial visualization skill is developed through life experiences ... children who are **exposed to appropriate learning environments** would have stronger spatial visualization skills later in life".* The question is: What is an appropriate learning environment?
The answer can be found in the following quote of an American genius and one of the Founding Fathers of the U.S. Benjamin Franklin who says:

"Tell me, and I forget.
Teach me, I may remember.
Involve me, and I learn".
Benjamin Franklin

Involvement of the students in the classroom **is an appropriate learning environment**, that Prof. Bertoline is suggesting, and in my view that is the most productive and most effective way to develop (improve) the visualization skill and make our students, not only at WMU, but at the national level, more successful in STEM, as well as more competitive on the international level. The strategy that I have been using to achieve this is based on using models to make a connection between the drawing and the object, but at the same time explaining to my students (based on the available time in the classroom) the manufacturing process and tools being used step by step to produce the final shape of the object. This strategy makes my students feel that engineering is "cool" and also makes them able to successfully handle more challenging design problems in subsequent subjects after completing my class.
The above strategy that I have been using in my classroom has proven to be effective and I tried to implement that strategy in this manual, which separates it from other Engineering Graphics textbooks. The other characteristic of this manual is that the AutoCAD topics are explained in the easiest possible way for students to understand and do the work in the lab or on their own time.
I use this opportunity to thank the following companies: **Autodesk Inc.**, for allowing me to use their programs, **Vac Developments, ON, CA** (supplier to the Aerospace / Defense industry), and **American Village Builders**, Portage, MI, for giving me permission to use some of their drawings, and **ICS Cutting Tools, Inc., Casco, WI**, that gave me permission to use the images of some tools from their Catalog.
I will greatly appreciate any comments or suggestion from anyone who reads this manual for the purpose of improving the quality of the next edition.

The Author

Table of Contents

Chapter 1

TYPES OF DRAWINGS

In the manufacturing industry Working Drawings are used in the process of manufacturing and assembling of parts. A Working Drawing could be a Detail Drawing, which is used for the purpose of making a part or an Assembly Drawing, which is used to put the parts together.

A DETAIL DRAWING has all necessary information for making a specific part. In some cases, a detail drawing might show more than one similar parts. A detail drawing normally has the following information:

1. Name of the part
2. Description of the shape
3. Dimensions and tolerances
4. Material, Surface finish, heat-treatment, notes and symbols (ex: welding)

A detail drawing of a simple part is shown below.

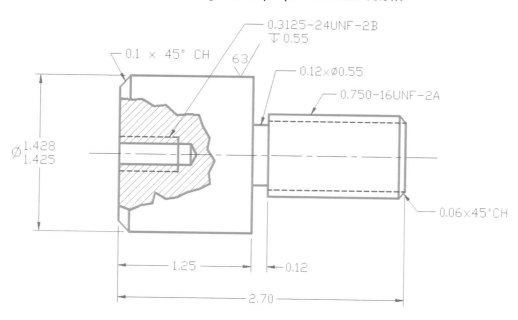

NOTE: BREAK ALL SHARP CORNERS

7

ASSEMBLY DRAWINGS are needed for the purpose of putting the parts together. The main difference between a detail and assembly drawing is that on an assembly drawing there are numerous parts that are numbered and shown in a table that is called a Parts List or BOM (Bill of Materials). BOM could be drawn as an extension of a title block, normally drawn above it or shown as a separate table usually drawn at the top right corner of a drawing. On an Assembly drawing the following information could be found:

1. Name of the assembly
2. Working relationship between the parts
3. BOM – Bill of Material *or* Parts List
4. Overall size (width, height and depth) of an assembly which is given for the purpose of checking if the assembly (big machine or mechanism) can fit the available space

The drawing shown on the next page is an assembly drawing of a Gear Box, which was designed and produced in VACDEVELOPEMENTS, ON, CA. This assembly drawing and the subassembly drawing (see Clutch Assembly- page 8) are reprinted courtesy of VAC DEVELOPMENTS.

Generally there are 4 types of assembly drawings:

1. *Sub-Assembly drawings* are used to show a single unit of a more complex mechanism or machine (ex: A Clutch of a Gear Box). See clutch subassembly drawing on page 9.
2. *Working assembly drawings* are a combination of a detail and an assembly drawing. They are used when a limited number of parts are used in an assembly and all of them could clearly be drawn and subsequently machined. Also the visual relationship between the parts is to be shown so that the parts can be easily put together using working assembly drawing.
3. *Diagram assembly drawings* are used to show a complicated structure in a simplified way by using symbols, which in AutoCAD are known as blocks and are located in the Design Center.
4. *Exploded Pictorial drawings* are used when:
   a. A very complicated mechanism has to be assembled, which might be challenging even for professionals if it not shown in an exploded form showing the sequence of putting the parts.
   b. A relatively simple structure has to be assembled (Ex: Furniture) by a non-professional. This is commonly practiced by furniture companies for the purpose of saving money on labor and for easy shipping.

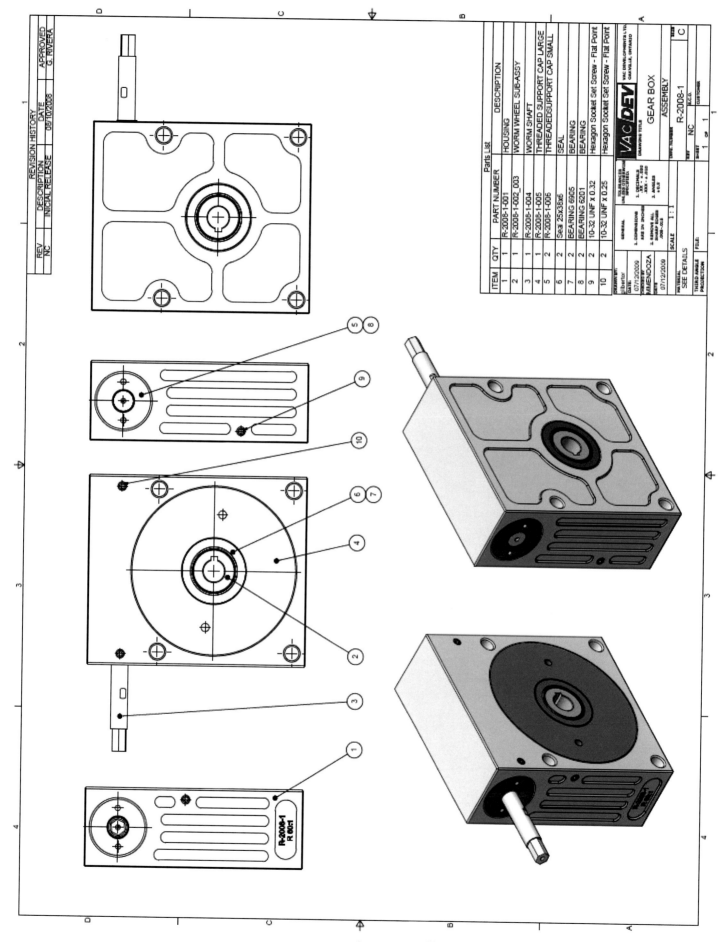

REVISION HISTORY

REV	DESCRIPTION	DATE	APPROVED
NC	INICIAL RELEASE	08/10/2008	G. RIVERA

Parts List

ITEM	QTY	PART NUMBER	DESCRIPTION
1	1	R-2008-1-001	HOUSING
2	1	R-2008-1-002_003	WORM WHEEL SUB-ASSY
3	1	R-2008-1-004	WORM SHAFT
4	1	R-2008-1-005	THREADED SUPPORT CAP LARGE
5	2	R-2008-1-006	THREADEDSUPPORT CAP SMALL
6	2	Seal 25x38x6	SEAL
7	2	BEARING 6905	BEARING
8	2	BEARING 6201	BEARING
9	2	10-32 UNF x 0.32	Hexagon Socket Set Screw - Flat Point
10	2	10-32 UNF x 0.25	Hexagon Socket Set Screw - Flat Point

VAC DEV
VAC DEVELOPMENTS LTD.
OAKVILLE, ONTARIO

DRAWING TITLE
GEAR BOX
ASSEMBLY

DWG. NUMBER: R-2008-1
REV: NC
SHEET 1 OF 1

GENERAL
1. DIMENSIONS ARE IN INCHES
   .XX ±.005
   .XXX ±.010
2. ANGLES ±0.5
3. REMOVE ALL SHARP EDGES
   .000-.015

TOLERANCES UNLESS OTHERWISE SPECIFIED

DRAWN BY: gilberto/
DATE: 07/12/2009
CHECKED BY: MMENDOOZA
DATE: 07/12/2009
MATERIAL: SEE DETAILS
FILED:
THIRD ANGLE PROJECTION

SCALE 1:1

SIZE C

R-2008-1
R 60:1

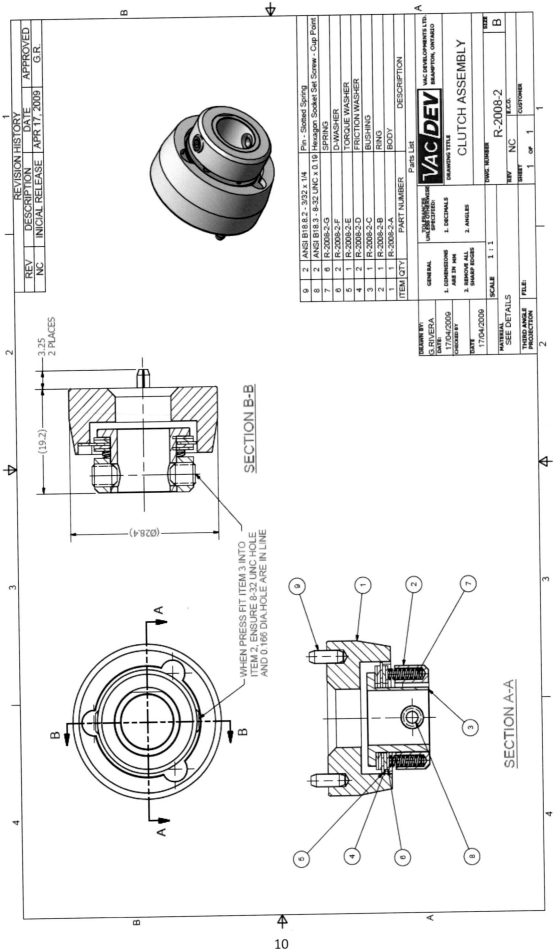

REVISION HISTORY

REV	DESCRIPTION	DATE	APPROVED
NC	INICIAL RELEASE	APR 17, 2009	G.R.

Parts List

ITEM	QTY	PART NUMBER	DESCRIPTION
9	2	ANSI B18.8.2 - 3/32 x 1/4	Pin - Slotted Spring
8	2	ANSI B18.3 - 8-32 UNC x 0.19	Hexagon Socket Set Screw - Cup Point
7	6	R-2008-2-G	SPRING
6	2	R-2008-2-F	D-WASHER
5	1	R-2008-2-E	TORQUE WASHER
4	2	R-2008-2-D	FRICTION WASHER
3	1	R-2008-2-C	BUSHING
2	1	R-2008-2-B	RING
1	1	R-2008-2-A	BODY

VAC DEV VAC DEVELOPMENTS LTD.
BRAMPTON, ONTARIO

DRAWING TITLE: CLUTCH ASSEMBLY

DWG. NUMBER: R-2008-2 SIZE: B

REV: NC E.C.O.

SHEET 1 OF 1

DRAWN BY: G. RIVERA
DATE: 17/04/2009
CHECKED BY:
DATE: 17/04/2009

MATERIAL: SEE DETAILS

THIRD ANGLE PROJECTION

TOLERANCES UNLESS OTHERWISE SPECIFIED:
1. DECIMALS
2. ANGLES

GENERAL
1. DIMENSIONS ARE IN MM
2. REMOVE ALL SHARP EDGES

SCALE 1 : 1

FILE:

SECTION B-B

3.25
2 PLACES

(19.2)

(Ø28.4)

WHEN PRESS FIT ITEM 3 INTO ITEM 2, ENSURE 8-32 UNC HOLE AND 0.166 DIA. HOLE ARE IN LINE

SECTION A-A

10

1.1 TITLE BLOCK

A Title Block is used to provide basic information about the part or assembly drawn on a drawing. It is normally located at the lower right corner of a drawing, so when a large size of a drawing is folded a Title Block can be seen. A standard Title Block according to ANSI (American National Standards Institute) with all the elements and dimensions is shown in the following image.

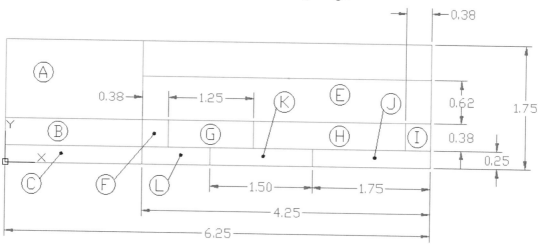

EDMM 1420 - Engineering Graphics title block elements and dimensions (according to ANSI standard title block for A, B, C drawing sizes)

```
A - Company/ School name
B - Department name
C - Course name/ Number
D - Drawing title/ Part name
E - Drawn By
F - Drawing Size
G - FSCN (Federal Supply Code for
      Manufactureer's)
H - Drawing Number
I - Revision
J - Sheet Number
K - Date
L - Scale
```

EDMM 1420 – Engineering Graphics title block elements and dimensions. A title Block with Text and all the requirements for assignment 4.4 is shown on the next page.

ENGINEERING GRAPHICS
Assignment 2.3 — (Manual)
Assignment 4.4 — (AutoCAD)
TITLE BLOCK AND TEXT

REQUIREMENTS:
DRAW THE TITLE BLOCK,
THIRD ANGLE ORTHOGRAPHIC PROJECTION SYMBOL
AND PLACE THE TEXT WITH YOUR NAME.

WESTERN MICHIGAN UNIVERSITY	DRAWING TITLE: *TITLE BLOCK AND A TEXT*			
	DRAWN BY:			
DEPARTMENT OF ENGINEERING	SIZE A	FSCN:	DWG NO. 4.4	REV
EDMM 1420	SCALE 1 : 1	DATE:	SHEET 1 OF 1	

1.2   LINE TYPES

VISIBLE (OBJECT) LINES are thick (0.7mm) lines that are used to represent visible edges and contours of a part.

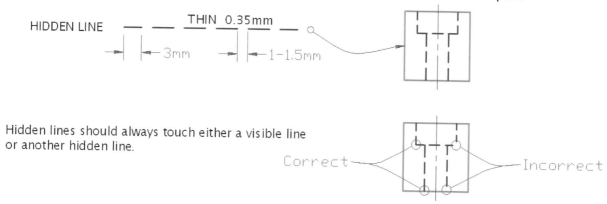

HIDDEN LINES are thin (0.35-0.5mm) lines that are used to show hidden features of a part.

Hidden lines should always touch either a visible line or another hidden line.

CENTER LINES are thin (0.25mm) lines that are used to indicate the axes of the symmetrical parts. Center lines are drawn as a long dash (about 20-50mm long) and a short dash (2-3mm long) based on the size of the drawing. They should be extended for about 3mm beyond the visible line. When center lines are used on circles or arcs they should intersect with short dashes*.

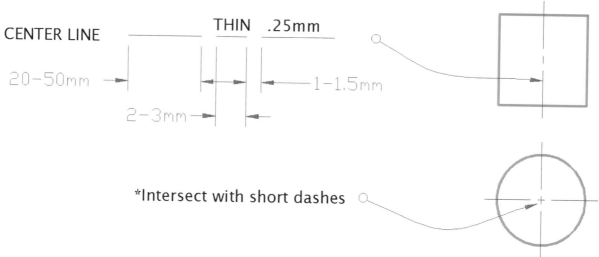

CUTTING PLANE LINES are thick (0.9mm) lines that are used to identify the imaginary cut (to indicate a cutting plane position) in order to create a sectional view.

VIEWING PLANE LINES are thick (0.7-0.9mm) lines that are attached to the ends of a Cutting Plane line showing the direction we should view the object in order to create a Sectional View.

SECTION LINES are thin (0.25mm) lines that are used to show the surface of an object cut by the "imaginary" Cutting Plane Line. Section lines are normally drawn at 45° and are spaced 2 to 3mm.

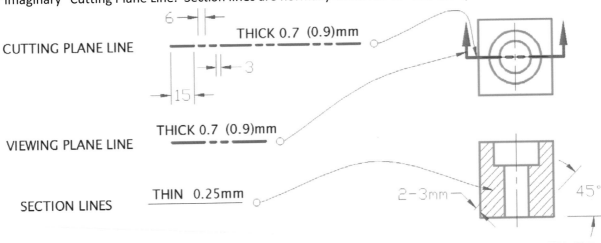

EXTENSION LINES are thin (0.35mm) lines that are used to indicate the termination of a dimension. Extension lines should start about 3mm from the object line representing an edge to be dimensioned and should be extended about 3mm beyond a dimension line (see drawing below).

DIMENSION LINES are thin (0.35mm) lines that are used to show the direction and the value of the dimension. If more than one Dimension Line is used, then the first Dimension Line should be a minimum of 10mm from the part outline, and the other dimensions should be placed at minimum 6mm apart.

Note: When dimensioning a number of concentric cylinders, dimensions should be placed in a staggered position for better clarity and easier focusing (see drawing on the right below).

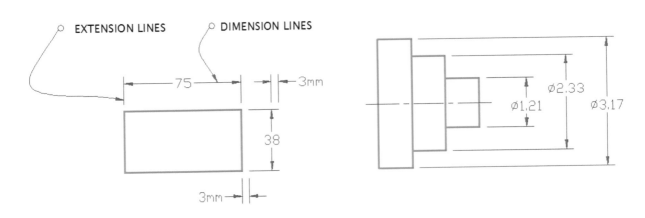

14

BREAK LINES include SHORT BREAK (0.7mm thick) and LONG BREAK (0.35mm thick). Break lines are used to limit a broken view of a section of a drawing. Short breaks are free hand drawn and are used on small parts. Long breaks are used on big parts and are straight lines with zigzag interruptions.

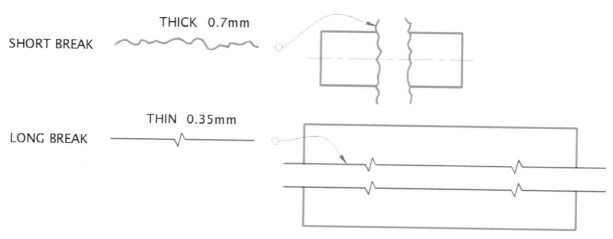

PHANTOM LINES are (0.35mm) lines that could be used to: 1) show a new position of a moving part – see image below. 2) Show a rough shape of a part before machining or 3) to draw a holding devise when drawn together with a part.

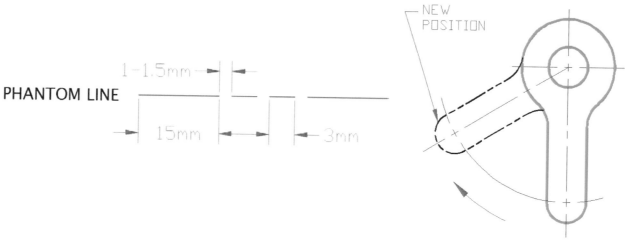

LEADER LINES are thin (0.25mm) lines that are used to put some notes in a specific position or show radial or diameter dimension. Leader lines could be drawn with an arrow pointing to a specific point or with a dot identifying a surface.

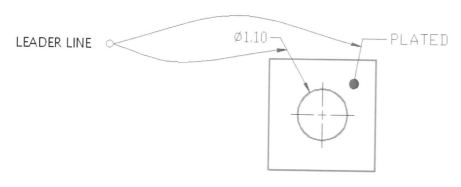

CONSTRUCTION LINES are thin (0.25mm) lines that are used to lay out the views and the dimensions on a drawing.

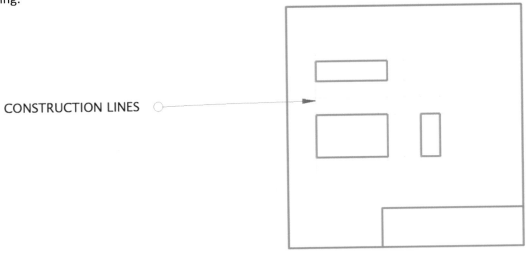

CONSTRUCTION LINES

ARROW SIZE (LENGTH - L) on a leader line and dimension lines has to be equal to the TEXT HEIGHT **(H)** on the drawing. The width of the arrow **(W)** has to be 1/3 of the length of the arrow.

$$L = H$$
$$W = \tfrac{1}{3} L$$

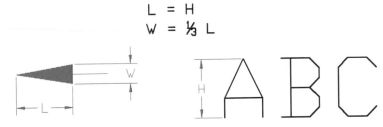

1.3   GEOMETRIC CONSTRUCTIONS

BISECTING A LINE - AB

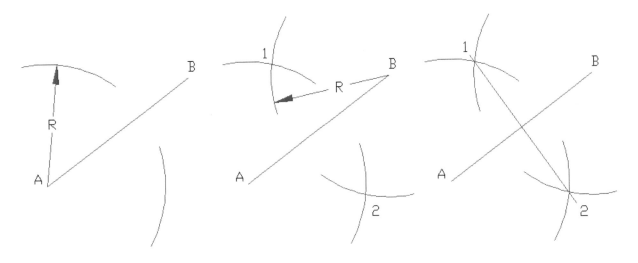

BISECTING AN ARC - AB

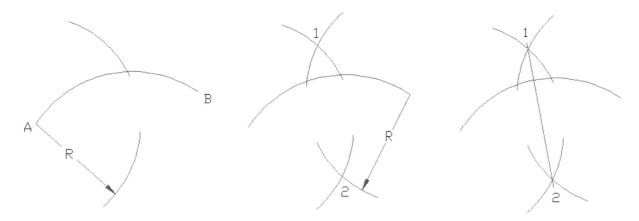

DIVIDING A LINE (AB) INTO 7 EQUAL PARTS

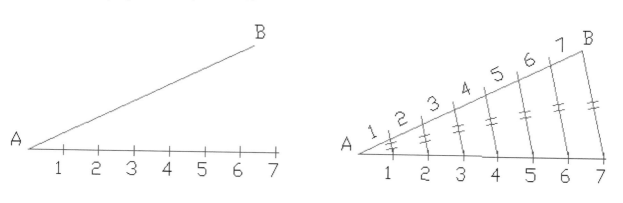

BISECTING AN ANGLE - ABC

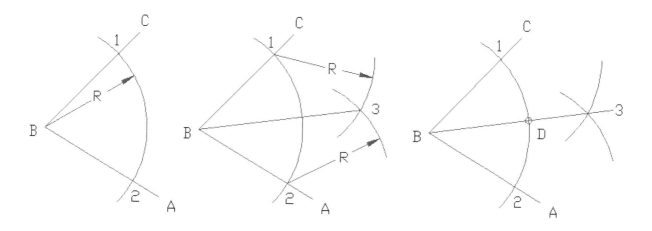

DRAWING A PERPENDICULAR LINE FROM A POINT (C) TO A LINE AB

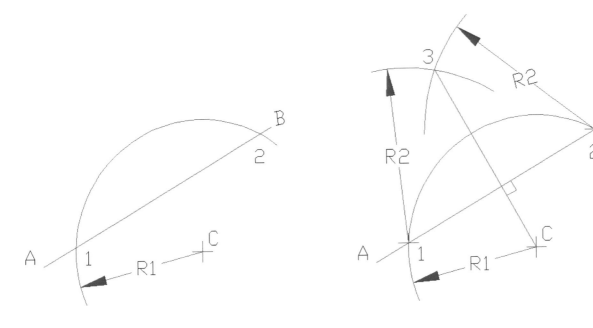

DRAWING A CIRCLE THROUGH POINTS 1, 2, AND 3

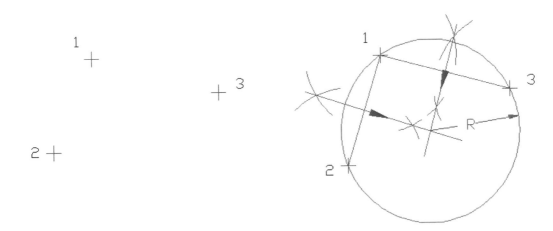

DRAWING AN EQUILATERAL TRIANGLE

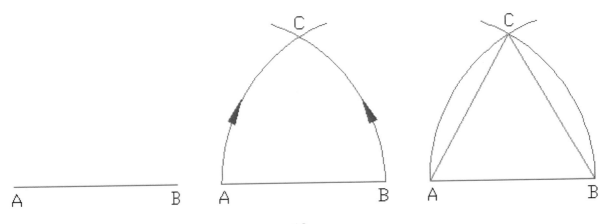

DRAWING A SQUARE

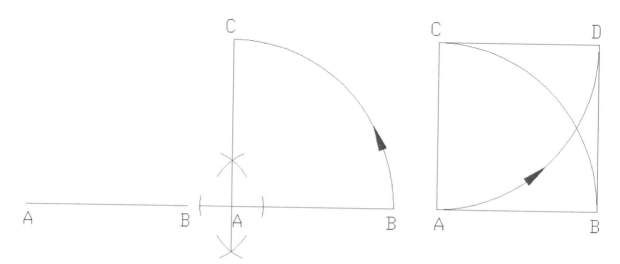

DRAWING A PENTAGON IN A CIRCLE

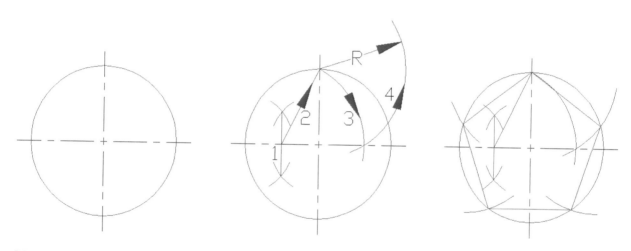

DRAWING A HEXAGON INSCRIBED IN A CIRCLE

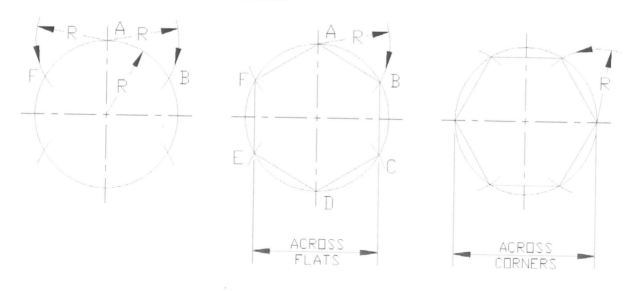

DRAWING A HEXAGON CIRCUMSCRIBED AROUND A CIRCLE

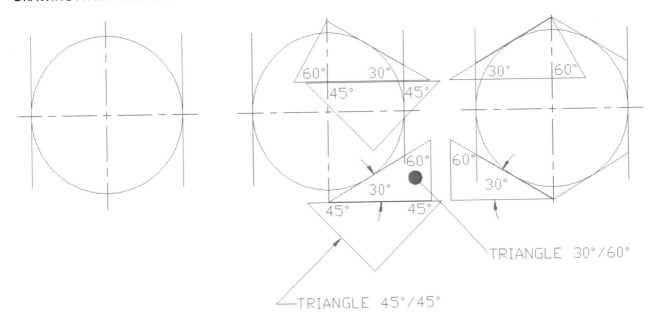

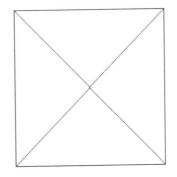
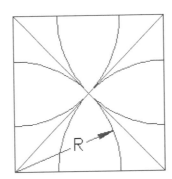
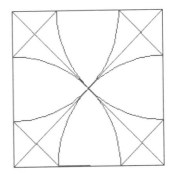

TRIANGLE 30°/60°

TRIANGLE 45°/45°

DRAWING AN OCTAGON IN A SQUARE

DRAWING AN ELLIPSE USING CONCENTRIC CIRCLES

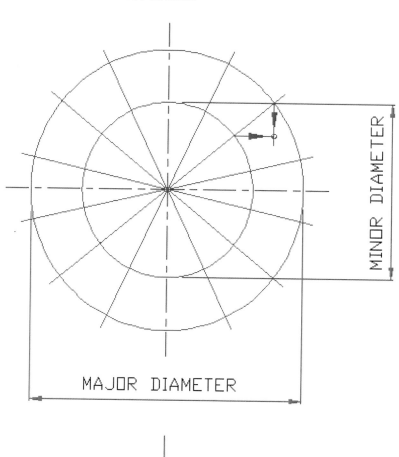

MAJOR DIAMETER

MINOR DIAMETER

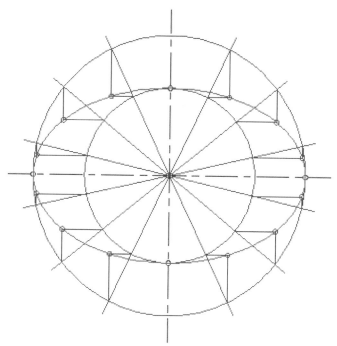

Chapter 2

INTRODUCTION OF AUTOCAD PROGRAM

2.1 STARTING UP AUTOCAD

- Click **Start** button
- Choose **All Programs**
- Choose **CAD | Autodesk | AutoCAD 2019 – English** (see the screen below)

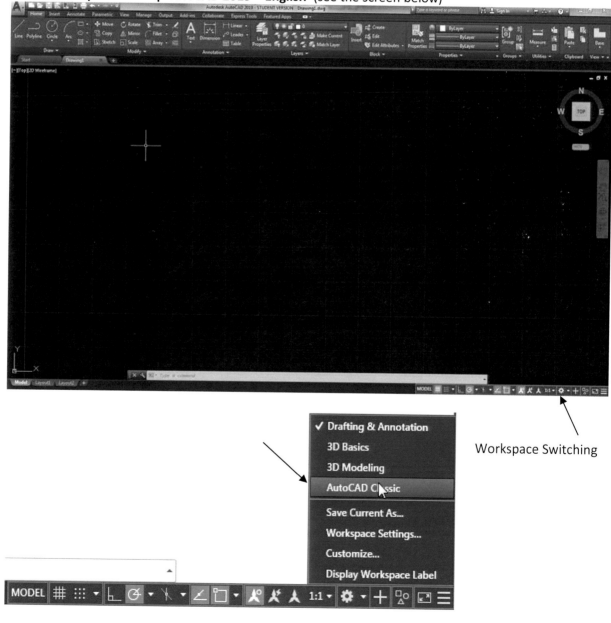

Workspace Switching

✓ **Drafting & Annotation**
  3D Basics
  3D Modeling
  AutoCAD Classic

  Save Current As...
  Workspace Settings...
  Customize...
  Display Workspace Label

- Click on **Workspace Switching**
- Choose **AutoCAD Classic** (see the screen below)

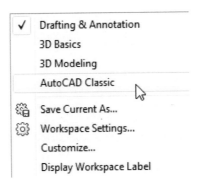

- Close **Tool Pallets**

2.2 STANDARD TOOLBARS LAYOUT

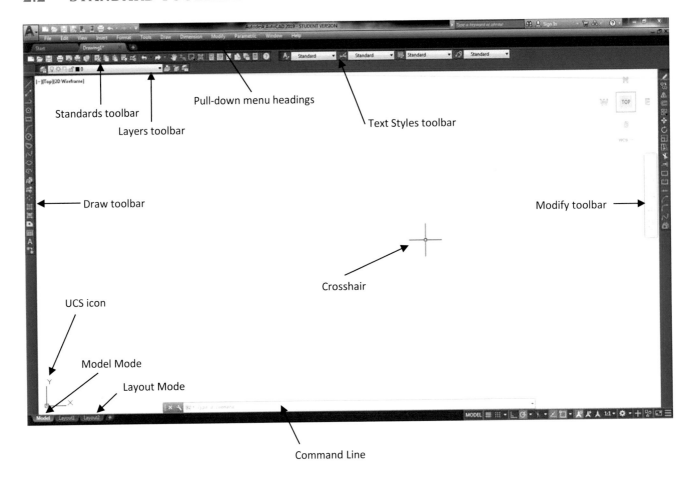

The standard toolbars that appear on the screen are not enough to create an AutoCAD drawing quickly and do not have all the elements needed for production. We need to have at least 2 more toolbars, the **Object Snap** and **Dimension** toolbars.

First, move the **Modify** toolbar from the right side of the screen to the left by clicking with the left button on the mouse in the area of the 2 short dashes at the top of the Modify toolbar. Holding the button down, move the toolbar to the left, align it with the Draw toolbar, and release it (see the screen layout below).

To open additional toolbars, right click with your mouse over any toolbar currently open. This will open the Toolbar menu (see screen on next page).

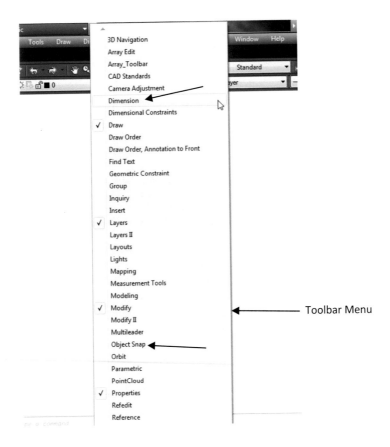

- Click on the **Dimension** Toolbar and place it to the right side of the screen
- Click on **Object Snap** Toolbar and place it beside the Dimension toolbar (see the Standard Layout with necessary toolbars on the screen on the next page)

Object Snap toolbar

Dimension toolbar

2.3 QUICK RIGHT-CLICK FOR ENTER SETUP

This setup is used to reduce AutoCAD user's time because with this setup the right mouse button can be used as the ENTER key.

Steps:

1. Click on **Tools**
2. Click on **Options**
3. Click on **User Preferences**
4. Click on **Right Click Customization**

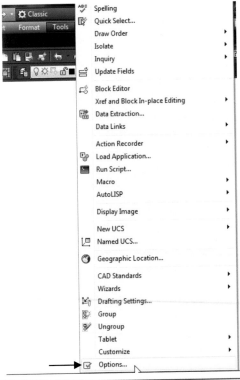

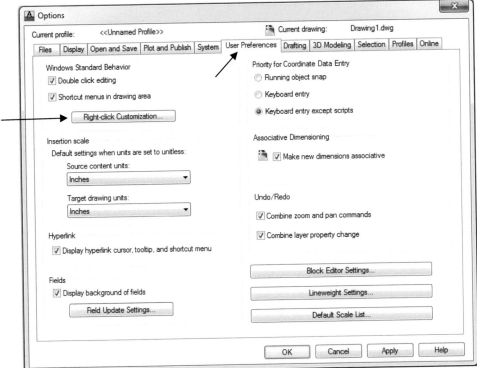

5. **Turn ON time-sensitive right click,** check box

6. Click on **Apply & Close**

7. Click on **OK** of the Options dialog box (see image on next page)

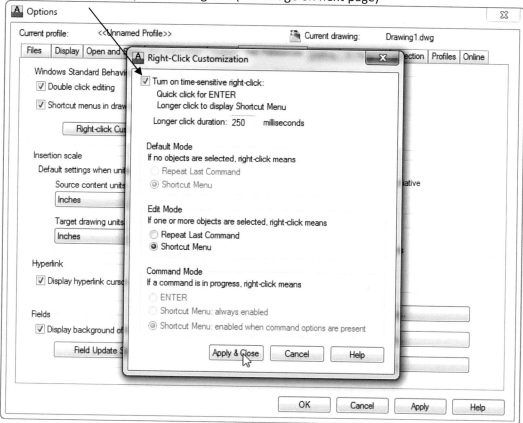

2.4 CHANGING THE COLOR OF THE SCREEN

1. Click on **Tools**

2. Click on **Options**

3. Click on **Display**

4. Click on **Colors** (see image on next page)

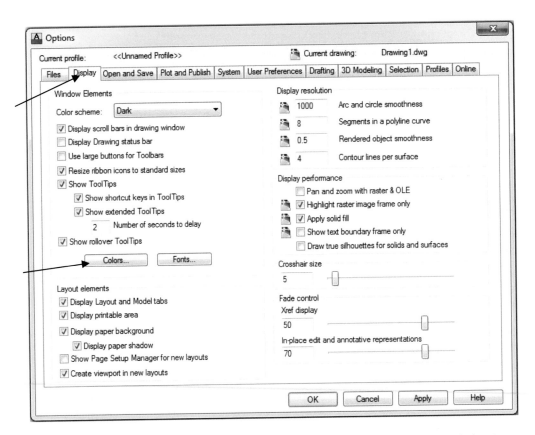

5. Click on the small selection arrow below the **Color** sign on the right side of the dialog box

6. Select the Color and click on the **Apply & Close** button (see following image)

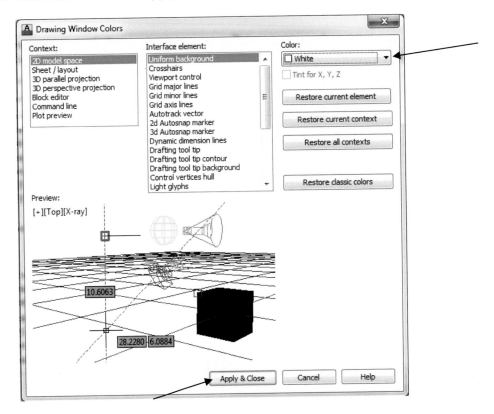

7. Click **OK** (see image below)

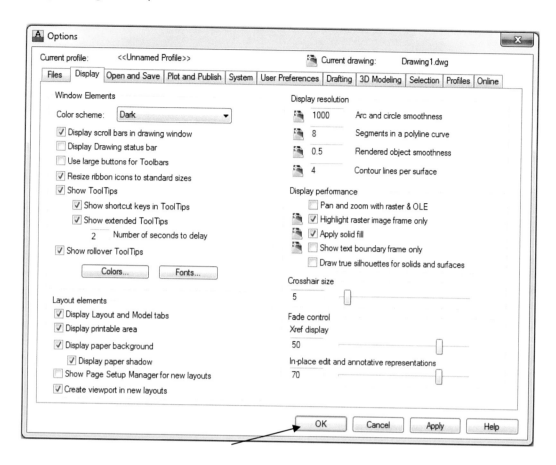

2.5   OPENING AN AUTOCAD DRAWING

Steps to open an existing AutoCAD drawing:

1. Click on the **Open** button (second button from the left on the Standard toolbar) – see below

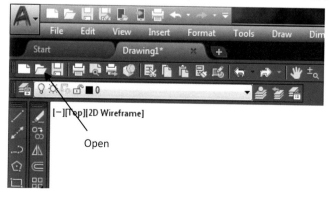

Open

2. Select the place where the drawing was saved (example: Flash drive, CD, a folder on the student network). Be certain to open the file which looks like either of the following files:

   Assignment 2.4 2D drawing.dwg   Assignment 2.4 2D drawing.dwg

3. Select the drawing and click **OPEN**

2.6   SAVING AN AUTOCAD DRAWING

1. Click on the **File** drop-down menu, scroll down and click **Save As** (see image below)

When saving files to the memory provided by the school, be sure to use the **I:** drive, which is listed as **studentData (I:)** (see following image). If a flash dive is available, files can be saved on there as well. When saving files, be sure to use the .dwg file; it has a symbol that looks like either one of the following: Assignment 2.4 2D drawing.dwg   Assignment 2.4 2D drawing.dwg

2.7   PRINTING AN AUTOCAD DRAWING

Although all AutoCAD EDMM 1420 assignments will be submitted electronically, here is the procedure for printing an AutoCAD drawing from a Model Space:

1. Click on the **Plot** button (fourth button from the left side on the Standard toolbar) – see below

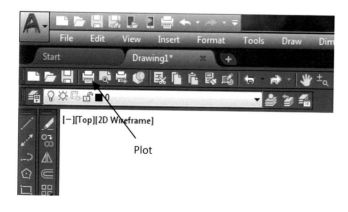

2. Select a **Printer Name** that you are connected to and then click **OK** (see image below)

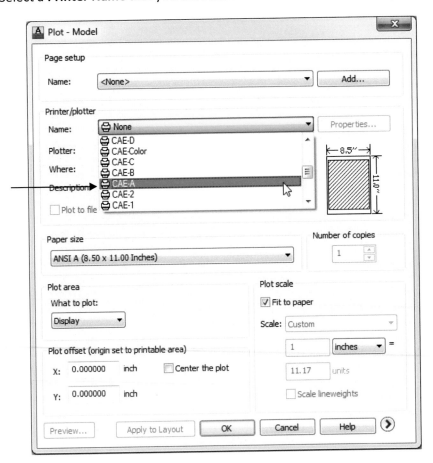

Chapter 3

ORTHOGRAPHIC PROJECTIONS

3.1   THIRD – ANGLE ORTHOGRAPHIC PROJECTION

For the purpose of seeing the part clearly we have to draw a certain number of views seeing the part from different sides. Generally there are 2 different approaches (called **First-angle** and **Third-angle** projection) in creating a drawing based on where the part is placed: in the First or the Third angle (quadrant). The First-angle orthographic projection is used in Europe and the Third-angle orthographic projection is used in the USA and Canada.

Using 2 planes (Horizontal and Vertical –see the drawing below) the space could be divided into 4 areas known as quadrants.

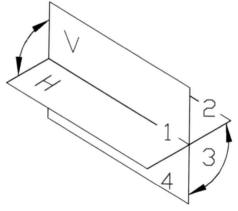

If we place the part into the 3rd quadrant it is called Third angle projection and if the part is in the first quadrant that is First angle projection. Looking at the part perpendicularly (at 90° or Orthogonally, which comes from Greek word *Orthogonios meaning Right angle)* from the Top, the image will be projected on a Horizontal plane and looking at the part from the Front, the image will be projected on a Vertical plane. By moving the standing bar away it will release the horizontal plane to rotate and align with the vertical plane (see the image on page 36). Aligned horizontal and vertical planes will show the top and front view of the part, which explains how a two-view drawing is going to be drawn always showing the top view at the top and the front view at the bottom of the drawing.

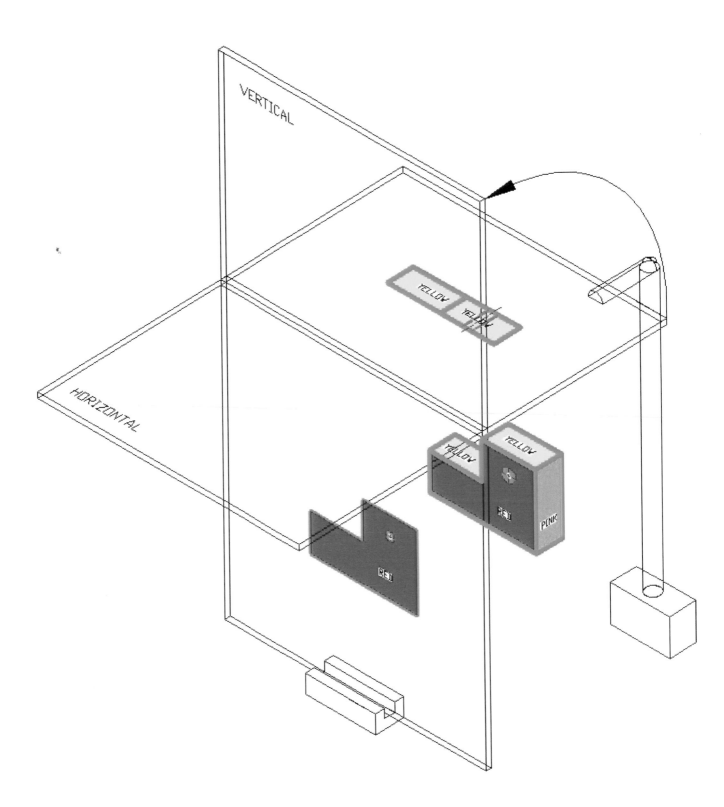

Principles in creating two basic views (Top and Front), using 3rd angle orthographic method.

If the part is complex then we have to create more than 2 views. For that purpose we will place the part into a projection box located in the 3rd quadrant enabling us to see the part projected from different sides (see picture on page 36).

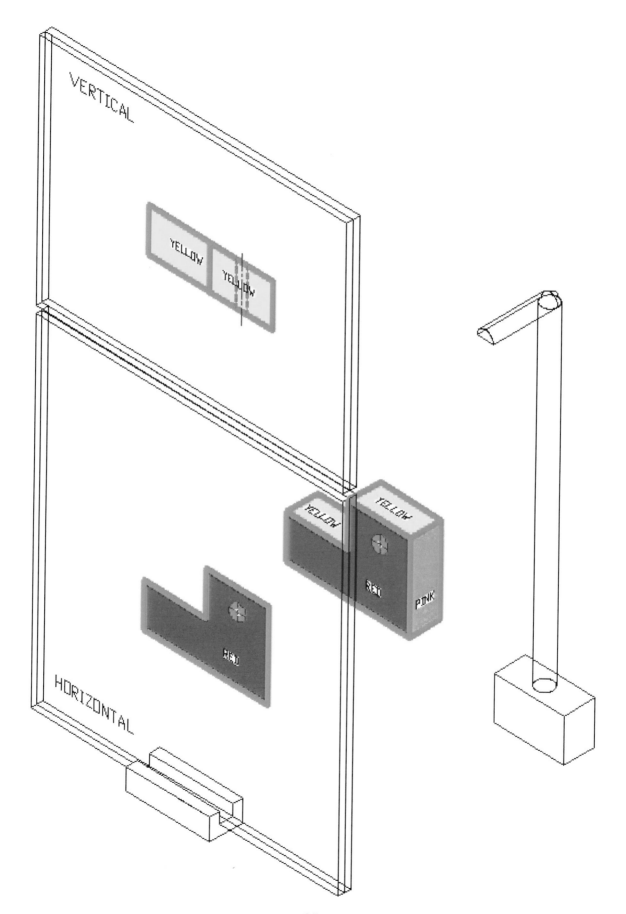

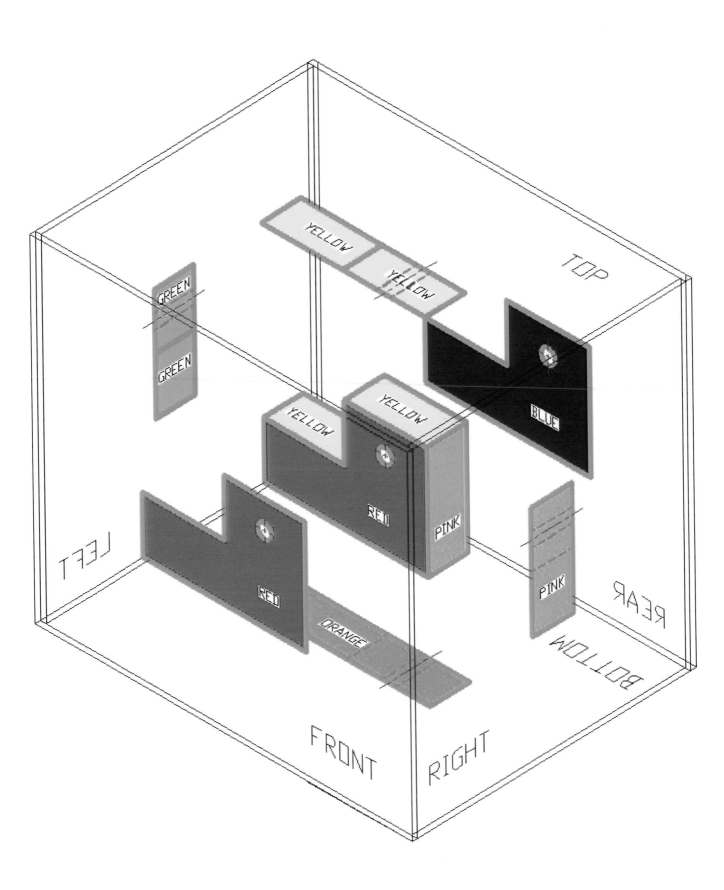

Using a projection box in the 3rd quadrant to see the object projected from different sides.

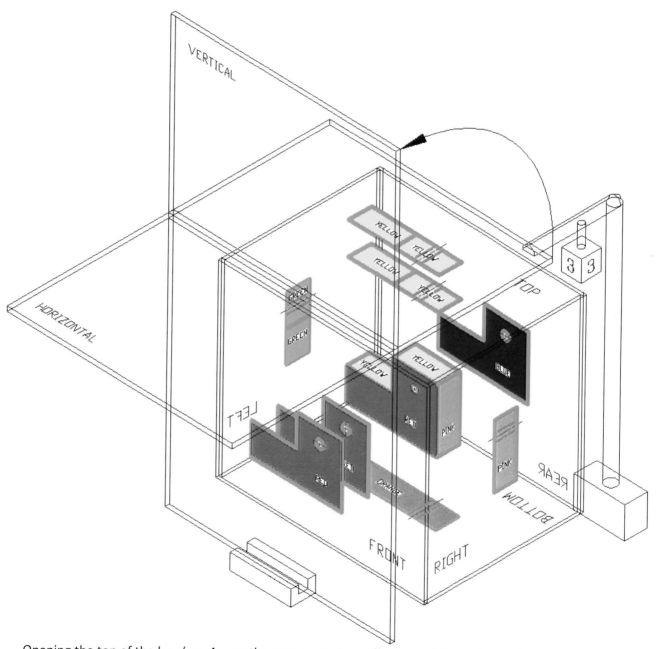

Opening the top of the box (see A – on the next page; normally Top and Front shows the 2-view drawing), opening the right side of the box shows 3-view drawing (top, front and right side - see B), C-(shows 4-view drawing), D-(5-view drawing) and E-(6-view drawing).

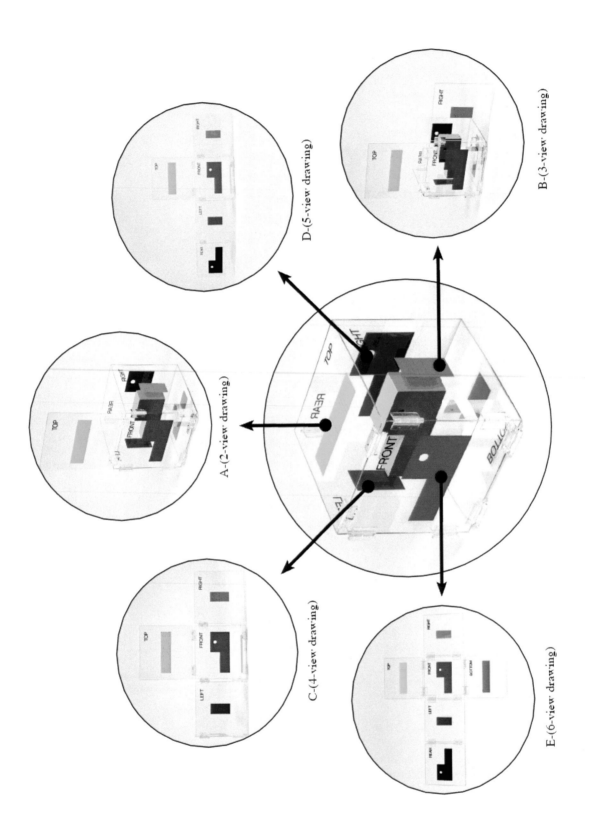

A-(2-view drawing)

B-(3-view drawing)

C-(4-view drawing)

D-(5-view drawing)

E-(6-view drawing)

Looking perpendicularly from different sides the part will be projected on the box creating 6 standard orthographic views:

1. Top view
2. Front view
3. Right side view (RSV)
4. Left side view
5. Bottom view
6. Rear view

The question is: How many views should we draw?

The rule we need to remember is: *We have to draw as many views as needed to describe the part clearly.*

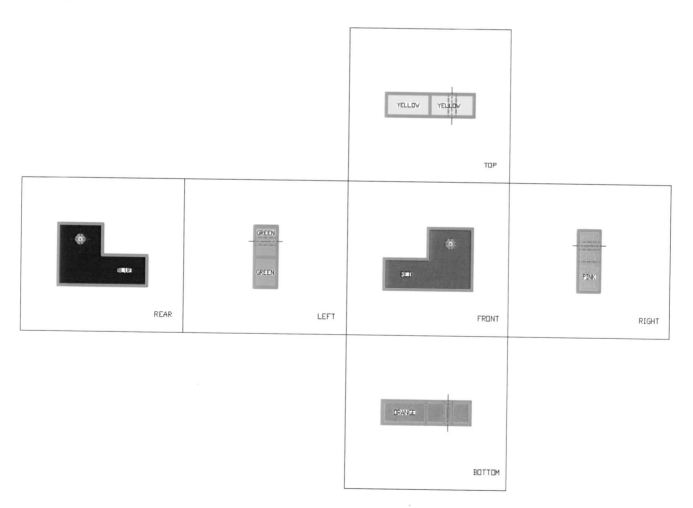

Chapter 4

STARTING A NEW DRAWING, PUTTING LINES ON A DRAWING AND USING UNDO AND REDO BUTTONS

4.1 STEPS IN STARTING A NEW DRAWING

Before putting any lines on a drawing we have to do the following steps:

1. To set **Units** click on **Format** and then click on **Units** (see below). Click on **OK** to accept Inch & Decimal Units. Click on the arrow beside Inches to select other types of units (ex: millimeters).

2. To set **Drawing Limits**

   2.1 Click on **Format,** and then

   2.2 Click on **Drawing Limits** (see below)

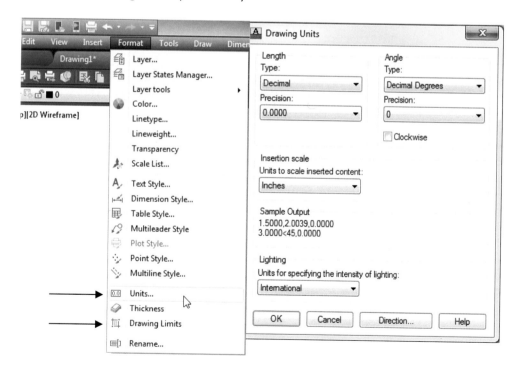

2.3 Specify lower left corner type: **0.0, 0.0** Hit **Enter**

2.4 Specify upper right corner type: **12.0, 9.0** Hit **Enter** if the size of the part drawn in scale 1:1 will fit on an 8.5" x 11" size paper. If the part will not fit, instead of accepting (12.0, 9.0) by hitting Enter, type in the MAXIMUM DIMENSION of the object multiplied by 2, then hit Enter (see below)

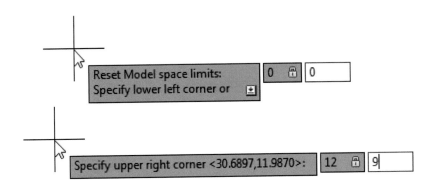

3. Select **Zoom All** (see below)

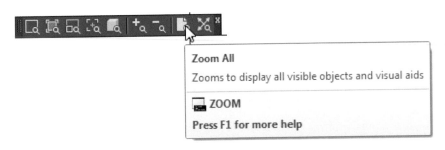

4.2   THREE METHODS OF DRAWING LINES

Using:

1. Absolute Coordinates
2. Relative Coordinates
3. Polar Coordinates

1. **Absolute Coordinates.** The Format for Absolute Coordinates requires having coordinates for each point always measured from the starting point (0,0).

Example: A (3,3)

B (7,3)

C (7,6)

D (3,6)

E (3,3) or

c – Enter to close the contour

42

2. **Relative Coordinates.** The Format for Relative Coordinates requires having the @ symbol followed by the distances in the X and Y directions measured relatively from the first point to the second point. The Format for Relative Coordinates is: **@4,0**

   Example: A (3,3)
   B (@4,0)
   C (@0,3)
   D (@-4,0)
   E (@0,-3) or
   c – Enter to close the contour

3. **Polar Coordinates.** The Format for Polar Coordinates requires having the @ symbol followed by the Length of the Line and its Orientation (0°, 90°, 180°, 270°). The Format for Polar Coordinates is: **@4<0**

   Example: A (3,3)
   B (@4<0°)
   C (@3<90°)
   D (@4<180°)
   E (@3<270°) or
   c – Enter to close the contour

Using any of the 3 methods explained above will make the same drawing, which is a 4 x 3 Rectangle (see image below).

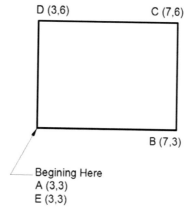

D (3,6)   C (7,6)

B (7,3)

Begining Here
A (3,3)
E (3,3)

4.3   DRAWING HORIZONTAL/VERTICAL LINES USING ORTHO COMMAND

To draw Horizontal or Vertical lines (Orthogonal Lines) we have to use **Ortho Mode**, which is the fourth button from the left below the command line (see image on the next page).

By having our Ortho Mode **ON** we can create the same rectangle shown above in the following way:

1. Click on the **Line** button
2. Specify **First** point: **type 3, 3** and hit **Enter**
3. Move your cursor to the right and type it: **4** and hit **Enter**
4. Move your cursor up and type it: **3** and hit **Enter**
5. Move your cursor to the left and type it: **4** and hit **Enter**
6. Move your cursor down and type it: **3** and **Hit Esc** button or just **Hit C** to close the contour of 4 x 3 rectangle (see image below)

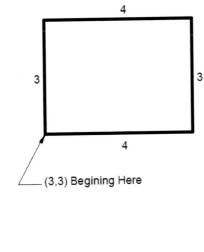

(3,3) Begining Here

4.4   DRAWING LINES AT AN ANGLE USING POLAR TRACKING COMMAND

To draw lines at any angle (including 90°) we have to use **Polar Tracking Mode**, which is located on the right of Ortho Mode (see image below).

Polar Tracking Settings:

In order to draw a line at a Specific angle (ex: 30°) we have to set the Polar Tracking to be at that angle. Here are the steps in that setting.

Polar Tracking

1. **Right Click** over Polar Tracking button
2. Select: **Settings** (see the image below)

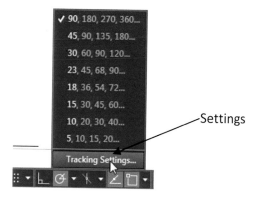

Settings

3. From the menu for Increments Angle **select: 30**
4. Click **OK** (see image below)

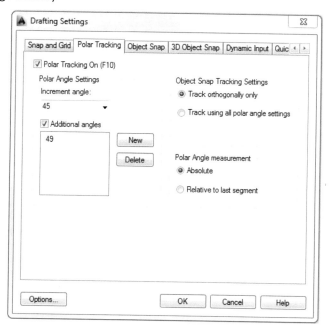

Drawing a Line at 30° angle

After doing the Polar Tracking Settings explained above and making sure that Ortho Mode is **Off**.

1. Click on the **Line** button
2. Specify First point: **Select a Point**
3. Specify next point: Select a Point and **Click** when you see an angle of 30° on the screen to specify the next point (see following image)

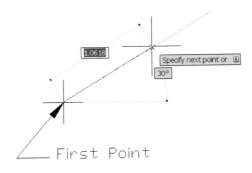

First Point

With the existing settings and increments of 30°, we can create lines at 30°; 60°; 90°; 120°; 150°; 180°; 210°; 240°; 270°; 300°; 330°; and 360°.

4.5   USING UNDO AND REDO BUTTONS

If we want to UNDO the last command we have to **Click** on the UNDO Button, which is located below the Draw button on the Standard toolbar (see image below).

The UNDO command could be repeated many times until we get to the starting command.

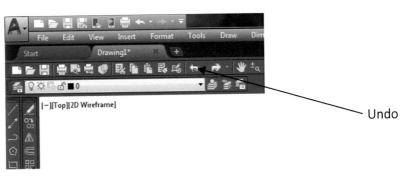

Undo

Sometimes, if we have backed up too far, it is necessary to reverse the last or several Undo commands by using the **REDO** button which is located right beside the Undo button. See the image below for the location of the REDO button.

Redo

Chapter 5

USING DRAW TOOLBAR

Draw Toolbar with the commands is shown below.

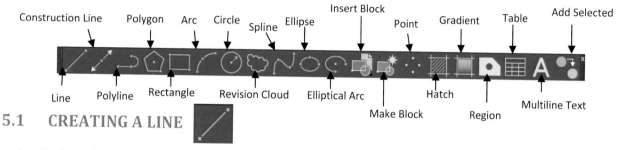

5.1 CREATING A LINE

1. Click on the **Line** button
2. Specify First point on the screen (enter the coordinates or Snap to a point)
3. Specify Next point (enter the coordinates or Snap to a point) – see image below

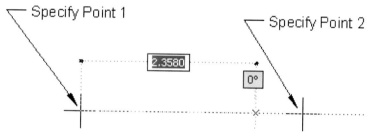

5.2 CONSTRUCTION LINE

1. Click on **Construction Line** button
2. Specify a Point
3. Specify Through point (normally at 0° – to create a horizontal construction line)
4. Specify Through point (at 90° – to create a vertical construction line) – see image on next page

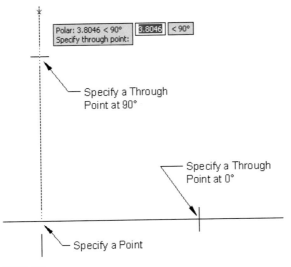

Polar: 3.8046 < 90°
Specify through point:

3.8046 < 90°

Specify a Through
Point at 90°

Specify a Through
Point at 0°

Specify a Point

5.3 POLYLINE

The **Polyline** command could be used to create a straight line(s), Arc(s), or Arrow(s). If more than 1 line, arc, or arrow is created using a polyline command, all entities are treated as one single entity. If we select one of them to be deleted, we will delete all of them.

Creating a Line using Polyline command

1. Click on **Polyline** button
2. Specify Start point
3. Specify Next point
4. Specify Next point (see image below)

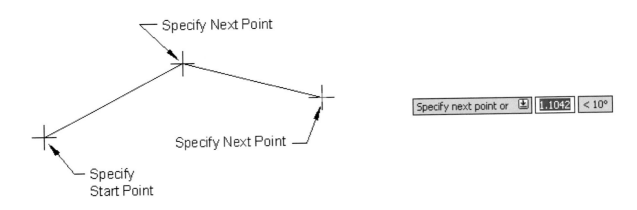

Specify Next Point

Specify next point or 1.1042 < 10°

Specify Next Point

Specify
Start Point

Creating an Arrow using Polyline command

1. Click on **Polyline** button
2. Specify Start point, (have your Ortho Mode ON – see image on next page)
3. Select and type it **W** (for Width)
4. Hit **Enter**
5. Specify Starting Width <0.000>: **Hit Enter**

6. Specify Ending Width <0.000>: Type **0.1** and hit **Enter**
7. Specify the Next point: **Select and Type it: L** (for Length) and hit **Enter**
8. Specify the Length of Line: **0.3** and **Hit Enter** (see image below)

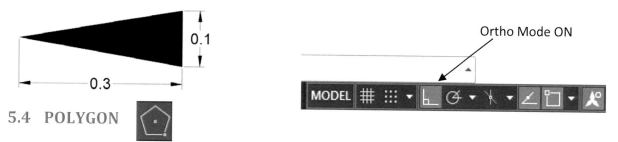

5.4 POLYGON

1. Click on **Polygon** button
2. Enter Number of Sides <4>: type **5** and hit **Enter**
3. Specify Center of Polygon: **Select a Point**
4. Enter an Option **<I for Inscribe>:** hit **Enter**
5. Specify Radius of Circle: type **3** and hit **Enter** – see the image of Pentagon inscribed in a circle with a radius of 3" below

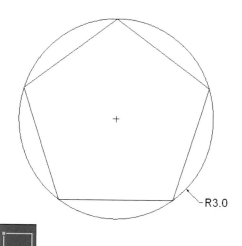

5.5 RECTANGLE

A **Rectangle** can be created by: a) using 2 corner points (explained below) or b) using the Area (if known) command, or c) Dimensions – Length and Width.

5.5.1 Creating a rectangle using 2 corner points

1. Click on **Rectangle** button
2. Specify First Corner point: **Select a Point**

3. Specify Other Corner point (see image below)

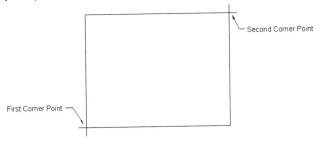

5.5.2 Creating a rectangle using its dimensions

1. Click on **Rectangle** button
2. Specify first corner point: **Select a Point**
3. Select other corner point or (Area/Dimensions/Rotation):
   :**Type D** for Dimensions and hit **Enter**
4. Specify length for Rectangle: **Type 6** and hit **Enter**
5. Specify width for rectangle: **Type 3** and hit **Enter**
6. Select one of the 4 positions that Rectangle could be located by clicking in the desired location (see image below)

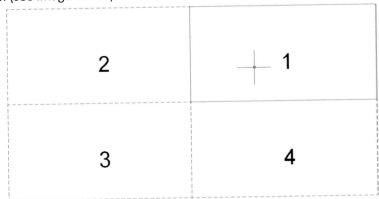

5.5.3 A rectangle can also be created (rotated) at a specific angle using the following steps:

1. Click on **Rectangle** button
2. Specify First Corner point: **Select a Point**
3. Specify Other Corner point: type **R** (for Rotation) and hit **Enter**
4. Specify Rotation Angle: **45°** and hit **Enter**
5. Specify Other Corner point (see image on next page)

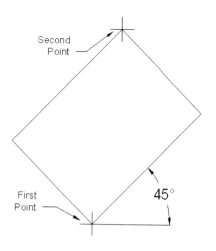

5.6 ARC

1. Click on the **Arc** button
2. Specify Start point of Arc: **Select a Point**
3. Specify Second Point of Arc: **Select a Point**
4. Specify End Point of Arc: **Select a Point** (see image below)

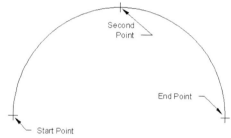

5.7 CIRCLE

A **Circle** can basically be created in 2 different ways: 1) By specifying Radius/Diameter or 2) Selecting one of the 3 options available (3P, 2P, or TTR option)

5.7.1 Creating a Circle specified by Radius

1. Click on **Circle** button
2. Specify Center Point: **Select a Point**
3. Specify Radius of Circle: type **3** and hit **Enter** (see image below)

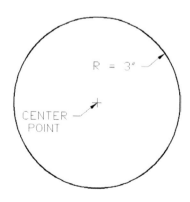

5.7.2 Creating a Circle specified by Diameter

1. Click on **Circle** button
2. Specify Center Point: **Select a Point**
3. Specify Radius of Circle: type **D** (for Diameter) and hit **Enter**
4. Specify Diameter of Circle: type **7** and hit **Enter** (see image below)

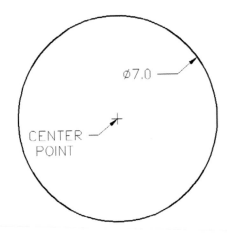

5.7.3 Creating a Circle using 3P points command

1. Click on **Circle** button
2. Type: **3P** (for 3 points) and hit **Enter**
3. Specify First Point on Circle: **Select a Point**
4. Specify Second Point on Circle: **Select a Point**
5. Specify Third Point on Circle: **Select a Point** (see image below)

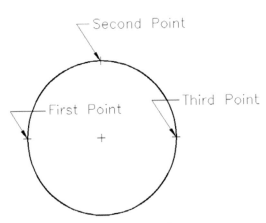

5.7.4 Creating a Circle using 2P points command

1. Click on **Circle** button
2. Type: **2P** (for 2 points) and hit **Enter**
3. Specify First End Point on circle's diameter: **Select a Point**
4. Specify Second Point on circle's diameter: **Select a Point** (see image on next page)

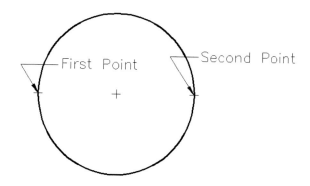

5.7.5 Creating a Circle using TTR (Tangent – Tangent – Radius) command

1. Click on the **Circle** button and create 2 circles with R = 3" and R = 5" (see image below)

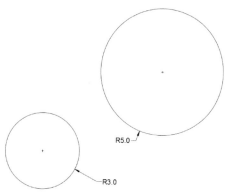

2. Click on **Circle** button
3. Type: **TTR** (standing for Tangent-Tangent-Radius) and **Hit Enter**
4. Specify Point on object for First Tangent of Circle: Select a Point – by **CLICKING** on the first Circle when you see this ⊙⤳ symbol
5. Specify Point on object for Second Tangent of Circle: Select a Point – by **CLICKING** on the second Circle when you see this ⊙⤳ symbol
6. Specify Radius of Circle: type **10** and hit **Enter** (see image below of a new Circle that has R = 10" and is tangent to the 2 previously created Circles)

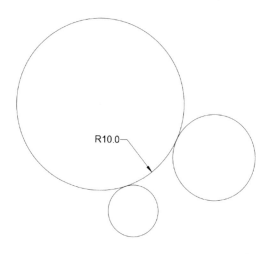

5.8 REVISION CLOUD

1. Click on **Revision Cloud** button
2. Specify starting point: **Select a Point**
3. Guide Crosshairs along Cloud Path: **Select points until you Close the Cloud Path** (see following image)

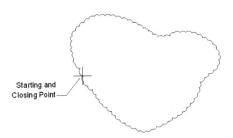

5.9 SPLINE

1. Click on the **Spline** button
2. Select first point: **Click** to specify the **first point**
3. Specify next point: **Click** in the position you like to specify the next **point (2)**
4. Specify next point: **Click** in the position you like to specify the next **point (3)**
5. Specify next point: **Click** in the position you like to specify the next **point (4)**
6. **Hit Enter 3 times** (see image below)

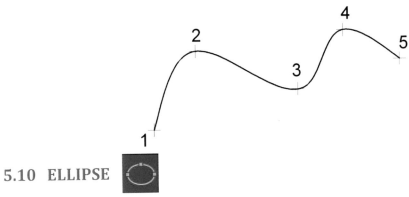

5.10 ELLIPSE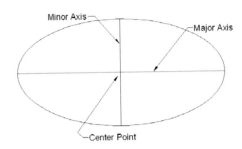

An Ellipse is defined by 2 Axes: the **Major axis** and the **Minor axis** (see image below)

1. Click on **Ellipse** button and have your **Ortho ON**
2. Specify axis Endpoint of ellipse: **Select a Point**
3. Specify Other Endpoint of axis: **Select a Point** or type **the Distance to Other Endpoint of First Axis** – see image below
4. Specify Distance to Other Axis: **Select a Point** or type **the Distance to Other Axis** (see the following image)

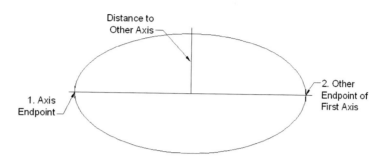

5.11 ELLIPTICAL ARC

1. Click on **Elliptical Arc** button
2. Specify axis Endpoint of Elliptical Arc: **Select a Point**
3. Specify Other Endpoint of axis: **Select a Point** or type **the Distance to Other Endpoint** of First Axis
4. Specify Distance to Other Axis: **Select a Point** or type **the Distance to Other Axis**
5. Specify Start Angle: **Select a Point** or type **the Value of the Start Angle** (ex: **45°** and **Hit Enter**) (see image below)
6. Specify End Angle: **Select a Point** or type **the Value of End Angle** (ex: **235°** and **Hit Enter**) – see image below

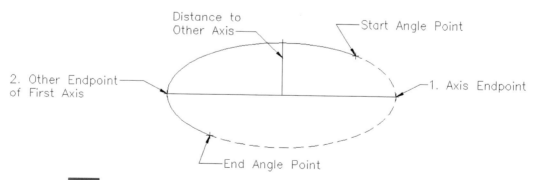

5.11 POINT

A **Point** is a Dot and is the smallest entity that can be drawn. Point Style can be a simple Dot or one of the following styles shown in the **Point Style dialog box** below.

To open the **Point Style dialog box** go to **Format** and select **Point Style** from the pull down menu and click OK – see image on next page.

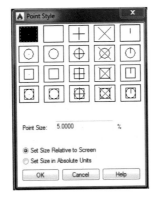

To Create a Point:

1. Click on the **Point** button from the Draw Toolbar
2. Specify a point

5.12 ADD SELECTED

1. Click on **Add Selected** button.
2. Select an Object on your drawing (example: Line, circle, rectangle, etc.)
3. By selecting a line on your drawing the **Line** command will be invoked and executed in a regular order starting with asking to specify the first point.

5.13 HATCH GRADIANT REGION TABLE AND MULTIPLE TEXT INSERT BLOCK MAKE BLOCK

Buttons will be explained in detail in specific chapters of the manual.

Chapter **6**

USING MODIFY TOOLBAR

The Modify Toolbar is shown below with the commands.

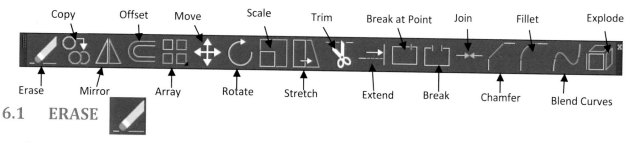

6.1 ERASE

The **Erase** command can be used in one of the following ways:

7.1.1 Erasing a single Line or Object

1. Click on the **Erase** button
2. Select a Line or Object
3. Hit **Enter** (see image below)

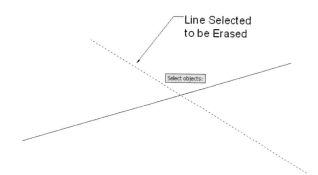

6.1.2 Erasing Several Lines or Objects using Erase Window

In selecting the Objects we can use one of the 2 following Erase Window options:

A) A Window from the Left Top Corner to the Right Bottom Corner will erase only the Objects that are completely inside the Erase Window. Notice that the window has a Blue color and its lines are Solid (see image on next page).

To Erase some Lines using the Erase Window:

1.   Click on **Erase** button
2.   Start creating a Window from the Left Top Corner to the Right Bottom Corner using the **Pickbox**

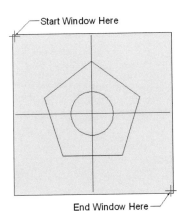

B)   A Window from the Right Bottom Corner to the Left Top Corner (also called a Crossing Window) will erase all Crossing Objects. Notice that this Window has a Green color and Hidden Lines (see image below).

To Erase some Lines using Crossing Window:

1.   Click on **Erase** button
2.   Start creating a Window from the Right Bottom Corner to the Left Top Corner using the **Pickbox**

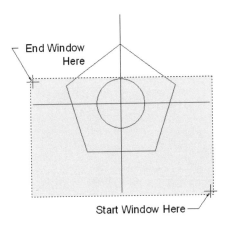

6.1.3   Erasing Some Lines/ Objects Using Window Polygon Command

1.   Click the **Erase** button
2.   Select Objects: type **WP** (for Window Polygon) and hit **Enter**
3.   First Polygon Point: **Select a Point**

4. Specify End Point of Line: **Select a Point**
5. Specify End Point: Continue selecting points until you close the window with the selected object(s) entirely inside the window
6. Hit **Enter** (see image below)

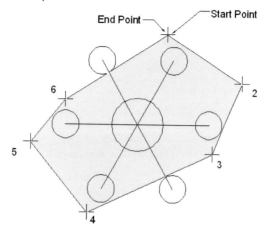

6.1.4 Erasing using Fence Command

1. Click the **Erase** button
2. Select Objects: type **F** (for Fence) and **Hit Enter**
3. Select first Fence point: **Select a Point**
4. Specify next Fence point: **Select a Point** and **Hit Enter** (the selected lines will become hidden). If the selection is correct then,
5. Hit **Enter** (see image below)

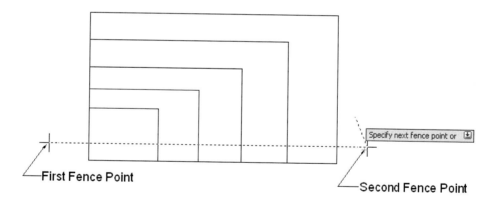

6.1.5 Erasing Everything

1. Click the **Erase** button
2. Select objects: type **All**
3. Select objects: hit **Enter** (all lines will become Hidden)
4. Select objects: hit **Enter** again

6.2 COPY A SINGLE OBJECT

1. Click on the Copy button
2. Select objects: Place the Pickbox over the circle and click to select

3. **Hit Enter** to finish selection
4. Specify base point or displacement: click anywhere to select the base point
5. Specify the location of the object being copied.

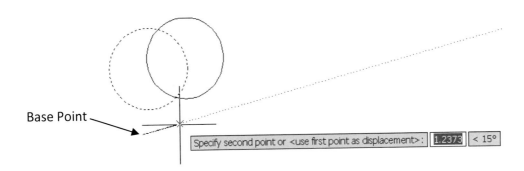

Base Point

Specify second point or <use first point as displacement> : | 1.2373 | | < 15°

6.2.1 Multiple copies of an object

1. Create a circle and a line as shown below
2. Click on the **Copy** button
3. Select objects: place the Pickbox over circle, **Click** to select
4. Hit **ENTER** to finish selection

5. Specify the base point: Go over the center of the circle and click when you see a little yellow circle (see image below).

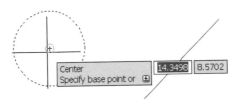

Center
Specify base point or ⊞ | 14.3498 | | 8.5702

6. Specify second point: Select the end of the line and click when you see yellow square (see image below).

Endpoint
Specify second point or <use first point as displacement> :

Endpoint
Specify second point or ⊞

7. Repeat step 6 by selecting the other end of the line for the second point
8. Hit **ENTER** to finish

6.3 MIRROR

1. Create a line and a rectangle as shown below

2. Click on the **Mirror** button
3. Select objects: Place the Pickbox over the rectangle and **Click** to select
4. Hit **ENTER** to finish selection
5. Specify first point of mirror line: go over the end of the line and **Click** when you see the yellow square

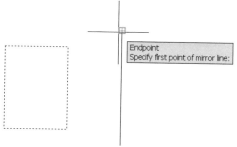

6. Specify second point of mirror line: go over the other end of the line and **Click** when you see the yellow square (see image below)

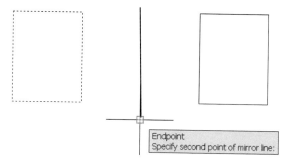

7. Erase source objects [Yes/No] <N>: Hit **Enter** to keep the source object (if you want to erase the source object type Y and hit **ENTER**)

NOTE: A mirror line could be any line defined by 2 points.

6.4 OFFSET

1. Create a line and a rectangle as shown below:

2. Click on the **OFFSET** button
3. Specify offset distance or Through: **Type 1** and hit **ENTER**
4. Select object to offset or<Exit>: Place the Pickbox over the line and **Click** to select
5. Specify point on side to offset or <Exit>: Place the cursor at any point on the right side (see image below)

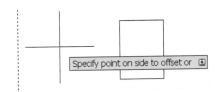

6. Click to accept that side, hit **ENTER** to complete function (see image below)

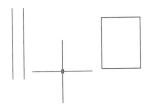

7. Repeat steps 2 – 6 on rectangle shape to create the image shown below

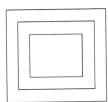

6.5 MOVE

1. Create a line and a circle as shown below

2. Click on the **Move** button
3. Select objects: Place the Pickbox over the circle and **Click** to select.
4. Specify base point or <Displacement>: Go over the center of the circle and **Click** when you see the yellow circle in the center (see image below)

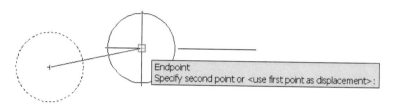

5. Specify second point or <use first point as displacement>: Go over the end of the line and **Click** when you see the yellow square (see image below)

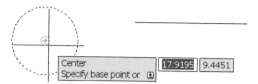

6. You just moved the circle to a new location (see image below)

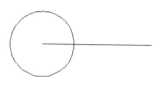

6.6   ROTATE

1. Create a rectangle as shown below

2. Click on the **Rotate** button
3. Select Objects: place the Pickbox over the rectangle and **Click** to select.
4. Hit **ENTER** to finish the selection
5. Specify base point: Select the lower left corner and **Click** when you see the yellow square (see image on next page)

6. Specify rotation angle or [Copy/Reference]<0>: **Type 45** and hit **ENTER**
7. Rectangle is now at **45°** (see image below)

6.7 SCALE

First you will create a 5x2 rectangle and then you will scale it to be twice the size (10x4).

1. Click on the **Rectangle** button from the draw toolbar
2. Specify first corner point or [ ]: **Click** anywhere to select the first corner and move the cursor to the right (see image below).

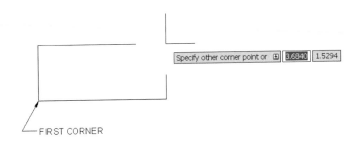

3. Specify other corner point or [Area/Dimensions/Rotation]: Type **D** (for Dimensions) and hit **ENTER**
4. Specify length for rectangle <10.00>: **Type 5** and hit **ENTER**
5. Specify Width for rectangle <10.00>: **Type 2** and hit **ENTER**
   You will see the image of a rectangle, which could be placed in one of the four positions (see image below)

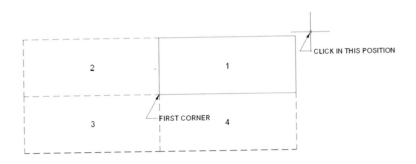

6. Move your cursor in position 1, 2, 3 and 4 to see the locations

7. Click when you are in position 1
8. Click on **Scale**  button
9. Select objects: **Click** on the rectangle and then Hit **ENTER**
10. Specify base point: Go over the lower left corner and click when you see the yellow square (see image below)

11. Specify scale factor or [Copy/Reference]<1.00>: Type **2** and Hit **ENTER**
12. You just created a 10x4 Rectangle (see image below)

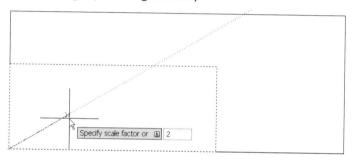

6.8   TRIM

1. Create a rectangle and two lines as shown below
2. Click on the **Trim** 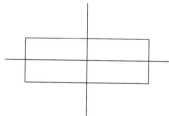 button
3. Select objects or <select all>: Hit **ENTER** to select all
4. Place the Pickbox over the extension of the line outside of the rectangle and **Click** (see image below)

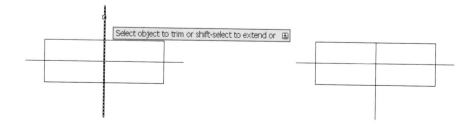

5. Repeat step 4 to trim the three remaining extensions (see image below)

6.9 EXTEND

1. Use the drawing above and add a rectangle to look as shown below

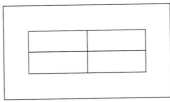

2. Click on the **Extend** button
3. Select objects or <select all>: Hit **ENTER** to select all
4. Place the Pick box over the line as shown below and **click**

   The line will be extended to the outer rectangle (see image below)

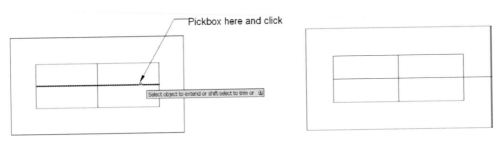

Pickbox here and click

Select object to extend or shift-select to trim or

5. Repeat step 4 to extend the other three sides to create an image as shown below

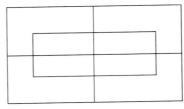

6.10 CHAMFER

A chamber is normally specified by two distances from a corner or by an angle and a distance. Both methods are explained below.

1. Create a 5"x2" rectangle as shown below

2. Click on the **Chamfer** 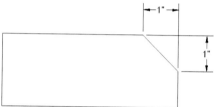 button
3. Select first line or [Undo/Polyline/Distance/Angle/Trim/Method/Multiple]:
   Type **D** (for Distance) and hit **ENTER**
4. Specify first chamfer Distance <0.000>: Type **1** and hit **ENTER**
5. Specify second chamfer distance <1.000>: Type **1** and hit **ENTER**
6. Select first line or [   ]: Place the Pickbox over the line as shown below and **Click**

7. Select second line or shift-select to apply corner: Place the Pickbox over the second line – above and **Click**
8. You just created a chamfer with first and second chamfer distance of 1" from the corner as shown below

Creating a chamfer using an ANGLE option

9. Click on the **CHAMFER** button
10. Select first line or [Undo/Polyline/Distance/Angle/Trim/Method/Multiple]:
    Type **A** (for angle) and hit **ENTER**
11. Specify chamfer length on the first line <0.000>: type **1** and hit **ENTER**
12. Specify chamfer angle from the first line <0>: Type **30** and hit **ENTER**
13. Select first line or [   ]: Place the Pickbox over the line as shown below and **Click**

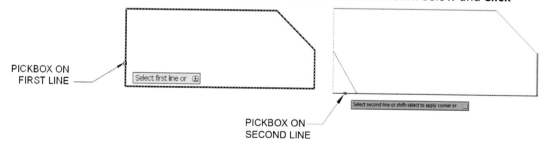

PICKBOX ON
FIRST LINE

PICKBOX ON
SECOND LINE

14. Select second line or shift-select to apply corner: Place the Pickbox over the second line – see above and **Click**
15. You just created a chamfer at a 30° angle to the first line (see following image)

30°

6.11 FILLET

Note: the previous drawing will be used to create a fillet.

1. Click on the **Fillet** button
2. Select first object or [Undo/Polyline/radius/Trim/Multiple]: Type **R** (for Radius) and hit **ENTER**
3. Specify Fillet Radius <0.000>: Type **.5** and hit **ENTER**
4. Select first object or [   ]: Place the Pickbox over the line as shown below and **Click**

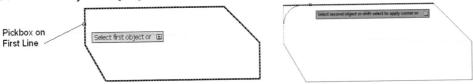

Pickbox on
First Line

Select first object or

Select second object or shift-select to apply corner or

5. Select second object or Shirt-Select to apply corner: Place the Pickbox over the second line – see above and **Click**
6. You just created a Fillet with a radius .5 (see image below)

Chapter 7

USING OBJECT SNAP TOOLBAR

Object Snap Toolbar with the commands is shown below.

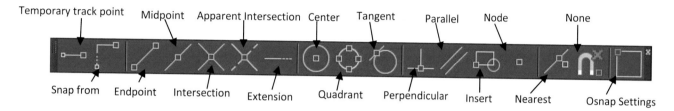

7.1 SNAP TO ENDPOINT

This command is used to snap to the closest endpoint of lines, arcs, splines, polyline segments, and corners (see image below).

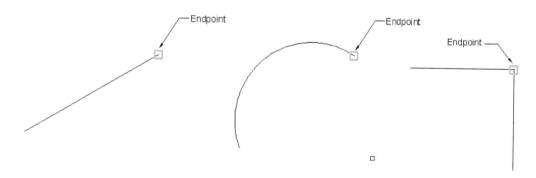

7.2 SNAP TO MIDPOINT

This command is used to snap to the closest midpoint of lines, arcs, splines, and polyline segments (see image on next page).

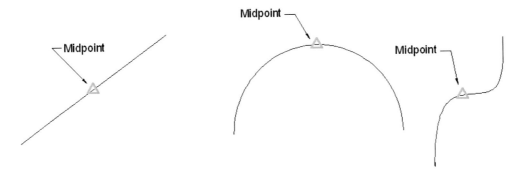

7.3 SNAP TO INTERSECTION

This command is used to snap to intersection of lines, shapes, and blocks (see image below).

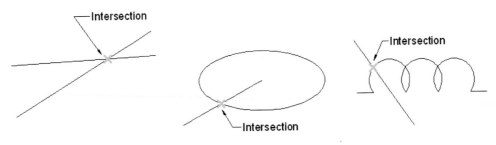

7.4 SNAP TO APPARENT INTERSECTION

This command is used to Intersect to the imaginary extensions of 2 lines. Steps in using this command when creating a Line:

1. Click on **Line command**
2. Click on Snap to **Apparent Intersection**
3. Specify first point: Click on the End point of the first line
4. With your cursor go over the other line until you see **X**
5. Click (see image below)

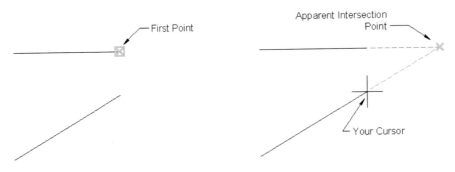

7.5 SNAP TO EXTENSION

This command is used to snap to the extension of an end point of a line at a specific distance. The distance and the angle can be seen on the Tooltip (see image below and 2 examples of using this command).

<u>Example 1</u>: Create a line Extended at 1.567 from the second point of the line and the end of the Arc.

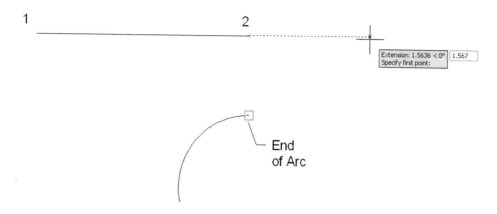

<u>Example 2</u>: Create a line at 1.2381 from the second point of an Arc to a point at 5.1561 and an angle of 35°.

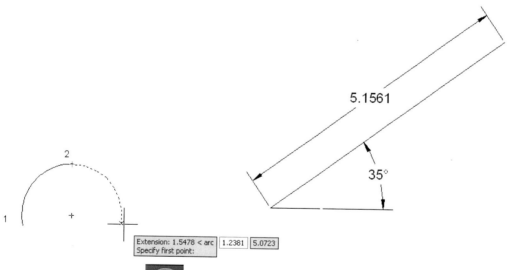

7.6 SNAP TO CENTER

This command is used to **Snap to the Center** point of Circles, Arcs, Ellipses, and Elliptical Arcs (see images on next page). Note, move your cursor over the edge of any circle, ellipse, or arc to display the center of that object.

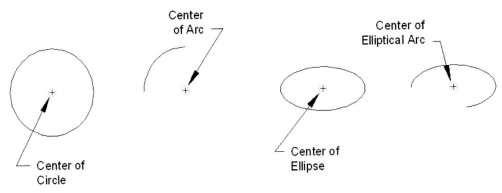
Center of Arc

Center of Elliptical Arc

Center of Ellipse

Center of Circle

7.7   SNAP TO QUADRANT

This command is used to Snap to one of the four points (located at 0°, 90°, 180°, and 270°) on Circles, Arcs, Ellipses, and Elliptical Arcs.

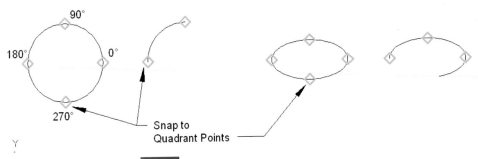

90°

180°   0°

270°

Snap to Quadrant Points

Y

7.8   SNAP TO TANGENT

This command is used to Snap to the Tangent points of Circles, Arcs, Ellipses, and Elliptical Arcs.

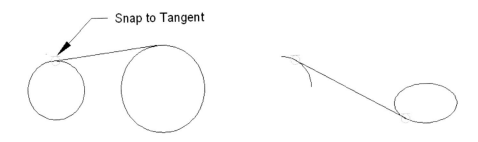

Snap to Tangent

7.9   SNAP TO PERPENDICULAR

This command, in most cases, is used to Snap to a point Perpendicular to a Line or a Circle, although it could be used to snap to an ellipse, spline, or polyline.

Snap to
Perpendicular

7.10 SNAP TO PARALLEL

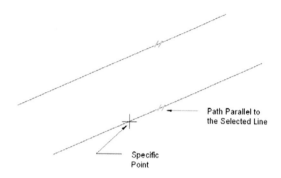

This command is used to create a Line starting at a specific point and Parallel to a selected line.

Path Parallel to
the Selected Line

Specific
Point

Chapter 8

LAYERS

Layers in AutoCAD play the role of transparent sheets used in manual drafting to draw different drawings and show/print all of them at the same time. Just as the semitransparent manual drawing can be taken out of the others and not be shown or printed, Layer(s) can also be turned OFF and not be seen on the screen. The purpose of Layers is to show specific entities that could be used individually or together with the entities on other layers to show the entire design. An example is a building which could be shown on one drawing having everything on it: Concrete base, Structural steel elements, Electrical wiring, Piping, and the other elements that make a functional building. All of these elements could be drawn on separate Layers so that we can have an Electrical Layer on which all electrical wiring is shown, which could be seen and printed as a separate drawing, although if needed, could still be shown/printed with the other Layers (See Foundation plan and Electrical wiring drawing respectively on next two pages with all symbols representing different electrical elements shown on electrical layer).

8.1   CREATING LAYERS

For educational purposes it is recommended to create the 5 basic Layers listed below. Although any color could be assigned to a specific Layer, it is recommended to use the 5 most frequently used colors shown in a bar starting with a Red Color – see step 4 on page 77 for Color Selection. As for the Line Type and Line Weight, ANSI and ISO standards are used.

5 Basic Layers

Name	Color	Line Type	Line Weight
Center	Red	Centerline	0.25
Hidden	Yellow	Hidden	0.35
Object	Green	Continuous	0.70
Text	Blue	Continuous	0.35
Dimension	Magenta	Continuous	0.25

Note: When selecting Center line or Hidden line you will notice that there are 3 Options [Center; Center(.5x); Center(2x)] and [Hidden; Hidden(.5x); Hidden(2x)] available. It is important to select the correct one based on the Size of the drawing (A, B, C, D or E). Normally (.5x) is used on small sizes and (2x) is used on bigger drawing sizes.

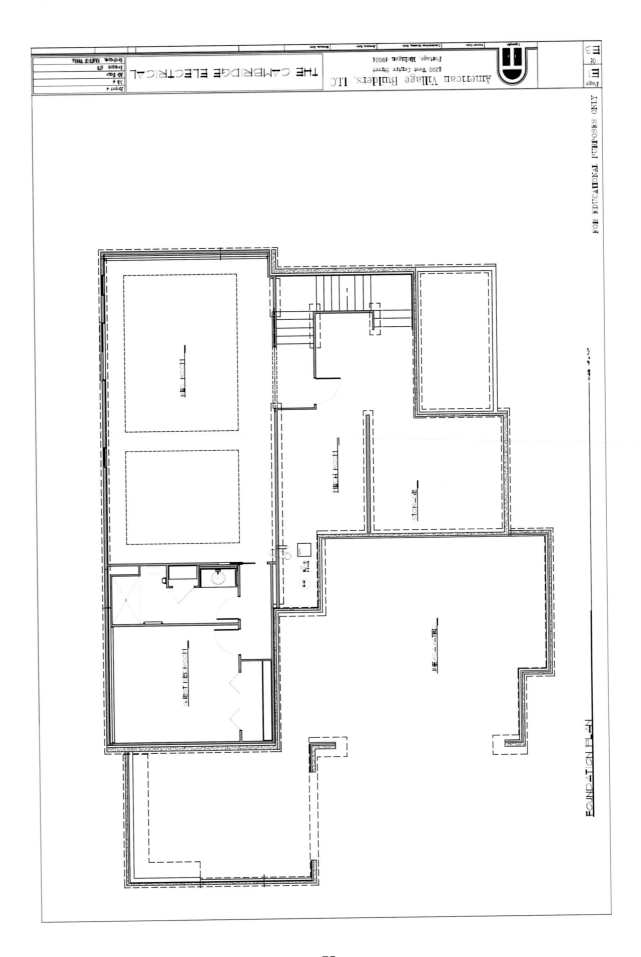

FOUNDATION PLAN

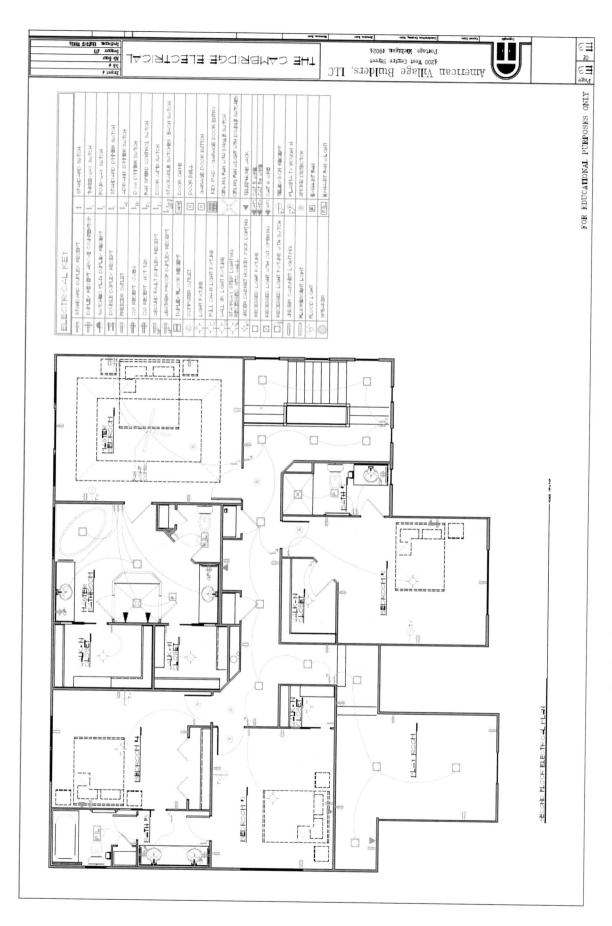

SECOND FLOOR ELECTRICAL PLAN

8.2   STEPS IN CREATING LAYERS:

1. Click on **Layer Property Manager** button – see image below for location

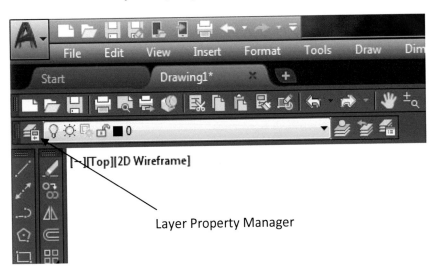

Layer Property Manager

2. Click on **New Layer** button

New Layer

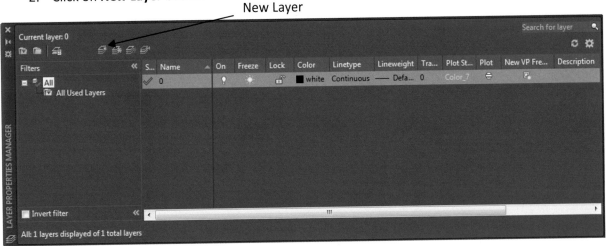

3. Under Name, In place of **Layer 1**, type: **Center line**
4. Click on ☐ under Color for this Layer. You will see **Select Color** dialog box (see image on next page)

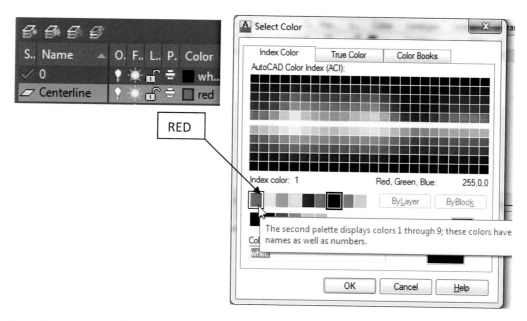

5. Select **Red** color and Click **OK**
6. Click on **Continuous** under Linetype – you will see the **Select Linetype** dialog box (see image below)

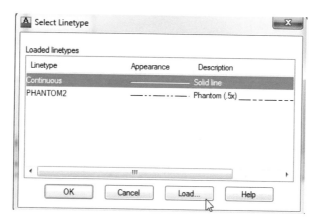

7. Click on **Load** – you will see **Load and Reload Linetypes** dialog box

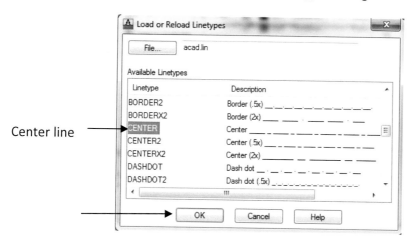

Center line

8. Scroll down and select **Center**
9. Click **OK**
10. Click on **Center** in the Select Linetype dialog box
11. Click **OK**

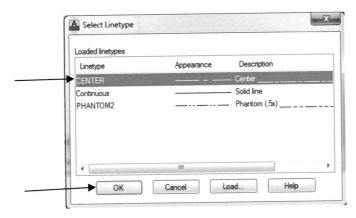

12. To select Line Weight: **Click** on the line – under Line Weight – you will see Lineweight dialog box

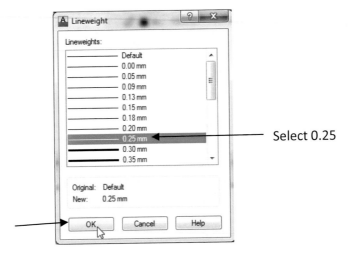

13. **Select 0.25**
14. Click **OK**

In AutoCAD there are three types of centerlines: **.5x**, **x**, and **2x** which are associated with the length of the size of the dashes in the centerline (selecting .5x will set the long dash to be 20mm in length and 2x will produce a long dash 50mm in length). The correct selection of one of the three different centerlines depends on the size of the paper which will be used to draw/plot the drawing. If we have a relatively small part that will be drawn on size A paper, then .5x centerline should be selected.

8.3   SETTING CURRENT LAYER

In order to create the other 4 Basic Layers repeat the steps from 2 to 14 using the Name, Color, Line Type, and Line Weight data for each Layer listed for the 5 Basic Layers above. After creating all 5 Layers you should have the image shown on the next page. Before you close the Layer Property Manager dialog box (by clicking on **X**), click on **Center line** Layer and then click on the green check mark ✔ (last in the row of new layer) in order to **Set Current** that layer and start using Center line Layer.

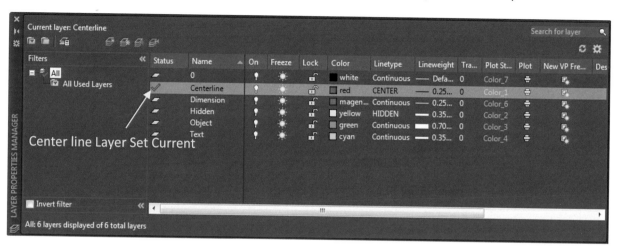

8.4   OPERATING WITH LAYERS

In the Layers Property Manager there are some functions that allow us to do the following things with layers:

- Turn a Layer **ON** or **OFF**. A Layer that is ON will appear on the screen and all entities on that layer will print/plot. If a layer is OFF the entities that are on that layer will not appear on the screen and will not print/plot.

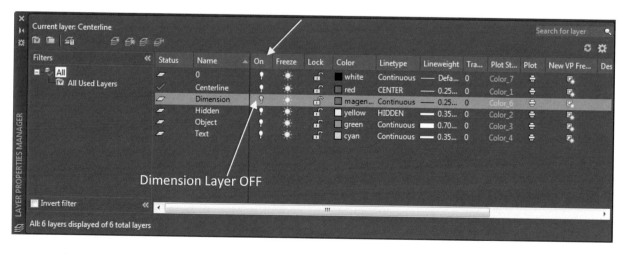

- The next Function is **Freeze** and **Thaw** function. The **Sun Icon** means the layer is thawed and all entities on that layer can be seen and printed/ plotted. The **Frozen** layer is shown with a snowflake icon and all entities drawn on that layer will not appear and will not print/plot.

The difference between the ON/OFF function and FREEZE/THAW function is that if a layer is **OFF** and if we do an **Erase All**, we will erase everything that was on that layer. If we do an **Erase All** on the layer that is **Frozen**, we will not be able to erase the entities on that layer.

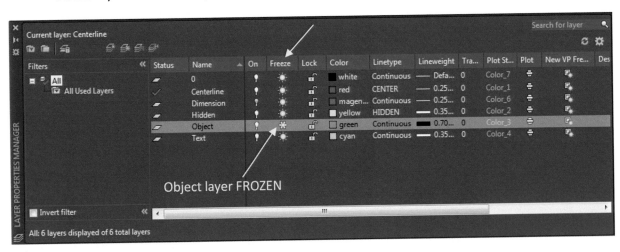

Object layer FROZEN

- **Locking** and **Unlocking** a layer. Entities that are on a Locked layer will appear on the screen, but cannot be edited or erased. Although a layer is locked we can still use the Object Snap tool bar to snap to the entities that are locked. When a layer is locked its color will slightly change on the screen. If we want to erase an entity, a padlock icon will appear right to the cursor indicating that entity/layer is locked.

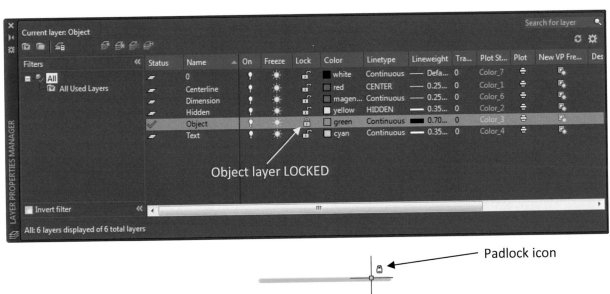

Object layer LOCKED

Padlock icon

- **Plot** function. If we click on the printer symbol under the Plot function for a specific layer we will see a red line crossing over the printer. The entities on that layer can be seen on the screen but will not print/plot.

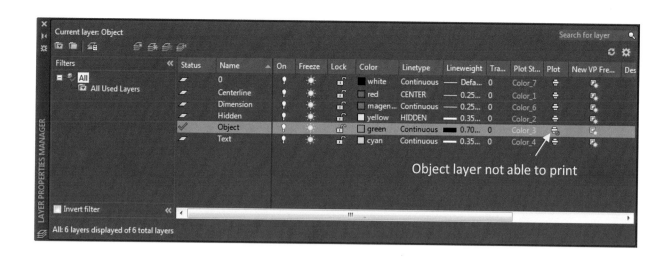

Object layer not able to print

Chapter **9**

TEXT STYLE

9.1 STEPS IN CREATING A NEW TEXT STYLE

1. Locate and click on the **Text Style Manager** button (see image below)

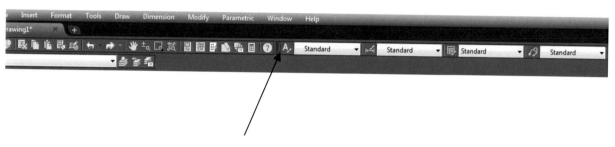

2. Click on the **New** button. Type **ROMANS** as a new Style Name and click **OK** (see image below)

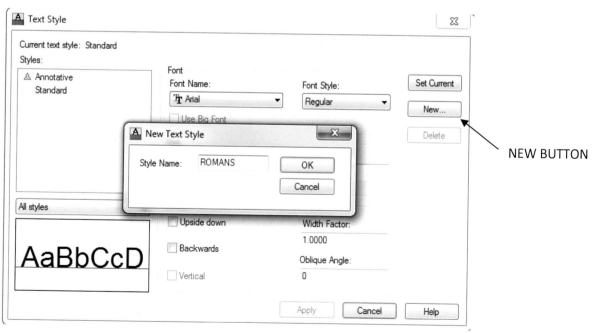

3. Select **romans.shx** as the font name for the ROMANS text style. Click on **Set Current** to change the current style (see following image)

4. Click on **Close** (see image below)

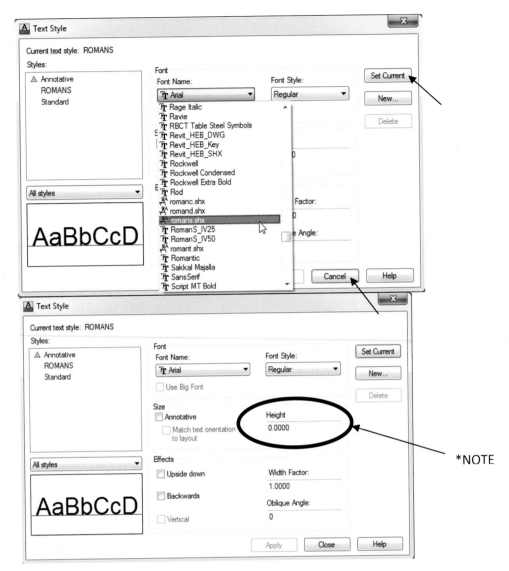

*NOTE

*NOTE: **DO NOT** set this value to anything but **0**, otherwise any text you put on the drawing will be that size regardless of the other settings you set in the drawing.

9.2   STEPS IN PLACING SINGLE LINE TEXT ON A DRAWING

1. Command: type it **DT** (for Dynamic Text)
2. Hit **ENTER**
3. Specify starting point of text (Justify/Style): **Click to a specific point**
4. Specify the height <0.2000>: **0.5** (or any other required Height)
5. Specify Rotation angle of text <0>: Hit **ENTER to accept 0 rotation angle and hit ENTER**
6. Type your Text
7. Hit **ENTER** twice

Note: Repeat the steps 1 to 7 by using **Height 0.7** (in step 4 and **Rotation Angle 45°** (in step 5)

When placing a note on a drawing it is a common situation that sometimes we need to put a special symbol (ex: Degree symbol °, Plus/minus sign ± or Diameter symbol Ø). The following are the codes that are used in AutoCAD to write special characters:

Code:	Symbol:	Meaning:
%%d	°	Degree symbol
%%p	±	Plus/minus sign
%%C	Ø	Diameter symbol
%%u	<u>text</u>	Text underlined
%%o	text	Text over lined

Example: To put the text **SHAFT Ø 5.75±.01** in your AutoCAD drawing, perform these steps:

1. Command: type **DT**
2. Specify the starting point of text: click to specify the starting point
3. Specify height<0.00>: type **.5** (or any other required Height)
4. Specify Rotation angle of text<0>: Hit **ENTER** (to accept 0 rotation angle)
5. Type: **SHAFT%%c5.75%%p.01**
6. Hit **ENTER** twice

All the above mentioned symbols (and much more) are available in the Character Map and could be used without typing a code which is explained below.

9.4 STEPS IN PLACING MULTIPLE LINE TEXT ON A DRAWING & USING SYMBOLS FROM A CHARACTER MAP

1. Command line: type **MT** (for Multiple Text) and Hit **ENTER**, or click on MULTIPLE TEXT button

   ![A] located near the bottom of the DRAW TOOLBAR
2. Click on the screen to **specify the First corner** and then the **Opposite corner** for the multiple text box (see image on next page)
3. Type your multiple line text and click **OK**
4.

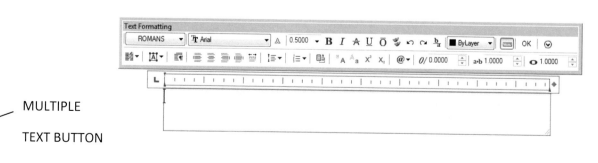

MULTIPLE

TEXT BUTTON

Note: If a special Symbol needs to be used follow the next steps.

5. With the cursor placed anywhere in the text box area Click on the Symbol button (see image below) and slide the cursor down on the cascade menu and at the bottom of the menu select **Other...** (Note that the most frequently used symbols are listed and can be selected directly without clicking on **Other...**)

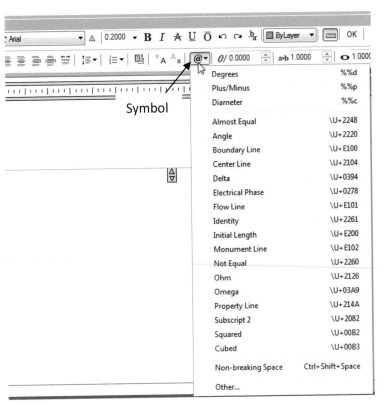

Symbol

5. Character Map will open (see image below)

6. Select any Symbol you need (Ex: Registered ® - see image below)

7. Click **Select** then click **Copy**

8. Close the Character Map by clicking on **X**

9. **Right Click** your mouse anywhere in the writing area you will see the following dialog box with the Paste option (see image below)

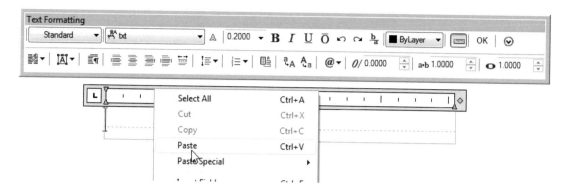

10. Click on **Paste** and you will see the Registered sign ® in the writing (Text) Area (see image below)

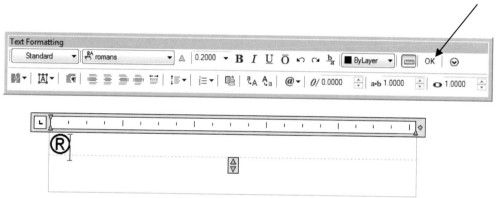

11. Click **OK** to close the MT (multiple Text) dialog box

9.5   ROTATION AND OBLIQUE ANGLE

Rotation Angle determines the angle at which the text will be placed. For example **0°** rotation angle will place the text in a horizontal position and **90°** rotation angle will place the text in a vertical position. Steps in placing text at **45°** rotation angle and the image of the text are shown below.

1. Command: type **DT** (for Dynamic Text)
2. Hit **ENTER**
3. Specify starting point of text (Justify/Style): **Click to a specific point**
4. Specify the height <0.2000>: **0.5** (or any other required Height)
5. Specify Rotation angle of text <0>: **45**
6. Hit **ENTER**
7. Type: **ENGINEERING**
8. Hit **ENTER** twice

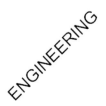

Oblique Angle also known as **Slant angle** shows the amount of Slant on the text. This angle could be positive, slanting the text to the right, or negative slanting the text to the left. The value of this angle could be from -85 to +85 and normally is about 68°. Zero slant angle will make the text upright. The value of the slant angle can be specified In the Text Formatting Dialog box when creating a multiple line text (see image below).

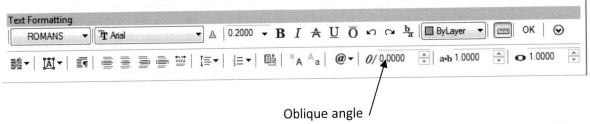

Oblique angle

If we want to have a text style with an Oblique angle, then we need to specify the value of the Oblique angle in the Text Style dialog box (see image below).

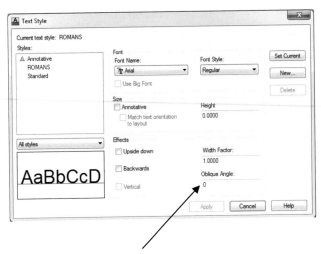

9.6   JUSTIFICATION OF TEXT

Justification is a positioning of the text based on the starting point. By default the starting point of the text is the lower left corner of the character. When placing Dynamic text there are 14 options for justification.

9.6.1 Align

1.   Command: type **DT**
2.   Hit **ENTER**
3.   Specify start point of text or (Justify/Style); type **J** and Hit **ENTER**
4.   Enter an option (Align/Fit/Center/Middle/Right/TL/TC/TR/ML/MC/MR/BL/BC/BR): Type **A** (for Align)
5.   Specify first point of text baseline: pick point 1
6.   Specify second point of text baseline: pick point 2
7.   Type your text (ex: **Engineering**)
8.   Hit **Enter** twice (see image below)

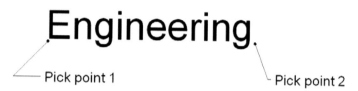

Note: The text will be aligned following the line starting with pick point 1 ending with pick point 2 which means that the sequence and position of pick points is very important. For example: if we use the same 2 pick points but we select them in reverse order, then the text will be upside down (see image below).

9.6.2 Fit

The **Fit** option works the same way as Aligned except that in Fit option **we have to specify the text height** and the AutoCAD program fits the text between the pick points without changing the text height. In Aligned option as you have noticed the text height does not need to be specified and changes based on the number of characters we type.

The meaning of the other options is shown and described below.

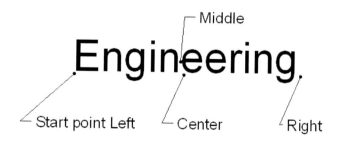

Justify option:	Meaning:
A	Align
F	Fit
C	Center
M	Middle
R	Right
TL	Top Left
TC	Top Center
TR	Top Right
ML	Middle Left
MC	Middle Center
MR	Middle Right
BL	Bottom Left
BC	Bottom Center
BR	Bottom Right

Chapter 10

ISOMETRIC DRAWINGS

Any view created using Third (or First) Angle Orthographic projection shows only 2 dimensions of a part. In order to see more dimensions we have to draw another view(s).

10.1 STEPS IN CREATING PROJECTION PLANES

We can see 3 dimensions in a single view if we create an Isometric View. The basics of the Isometric drawing are the 3 principal projection planes (Horizontal, Frontal and Profile) that are determined by 3 axes that make equal angles of 120° between them. The steps in **manually creating** the 3 axes and the 3 Projection Planes are shown below.

1. Create a vertical line of 2"
2. At the top end of the line create a circle with a radius of 1"
3. Keeping the 1" radius opening on your compass, make 2 arcs on the left and 2 arcs on the right side of the circle (see following image)
4. Connect the top end of the vertical line with the intersection to the left by drawing a line of 2"
5. Repeat step 4 by drawing a line of 2" to the right
6. Using your triangles, draw parallel lines to the 3 axes and create a cube with the size W = 2", H = 2" and D = 2"
7. You have just created 3 principal projection planes: Horizontal, Frontal and Profile (see following image)

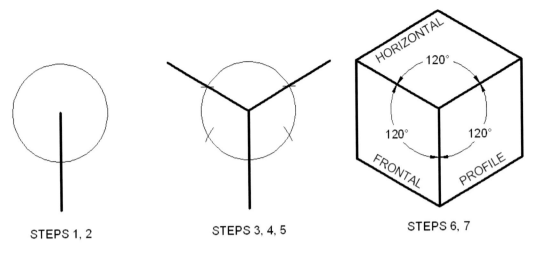

STEPS 1, 2   STEPS 3, 4, 5   STEPS 6, 7

Following the steps described above, create an Isometric View of a Step Block with dimensions ☆ W = 3", H = 2" and D = 1", with a step at W = 1.5" and H = 1" (see image below)

☆ W-Width, H-Height, D-Depth

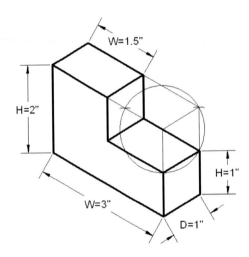

If the Block shown above has a sloped surface at distance of W = 1.5" and H = 1" instead of a step, then the 2 lines (at W = 1.5" and H = 1") should be connected forming a sloped surface as shown below.

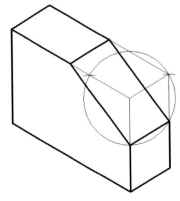

10.2 STEPS FOR CREATING AN ELLIPSE IN THE HORIZONTAL PROJECTION PLANE

1. Create a Horizontal projection plane with the size of 2" x 2" (see image on next page)

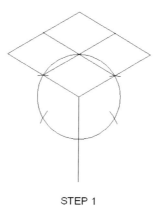

STEP 1

2. Draw lines 1 - 2; 1 - 3; and 4 - 5; 4 - 6 from each of the 2 corners (with shorter distance) of the diamond shape to the midpoint of each side as shown below.

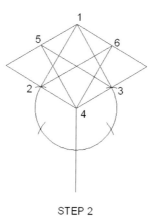

STEP 2

3. From the intersecting point A make an arc with radius R_1 connecting 2 and 5, and from point B an arc connecting 3 and 6

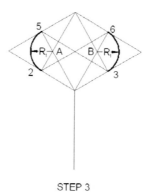

STEP 3

93

4. From point 1 make an arc with radius R_2 connecting 2 and 3, and from point 4 an arc connecting 5 and 6

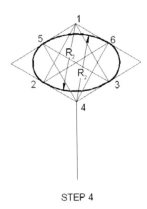

STEP 4

10.3 CREATING A CYLINDER

Creating Ellipses on the other 2 principal projection planes (Frontal and Profile) and creating a Cylinder using 2 horizontal projection planes is shown below.

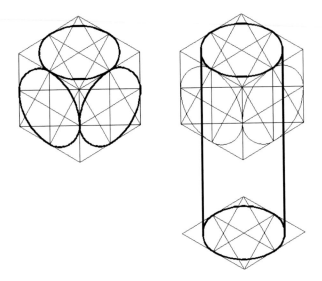

In an isometric drawing the back portion of the bottom ellipse should not be drawn – see image below.

Chapter 11

ISOMETRIC AUTOCAD DRAWINGS

11.1 STEPS IN ISOMETRIC AUTOCAD DRAWING SETUP

1. Click on **Tools** from the menu bar
2. From the pull down menu select **Drafting Settings** (see image below)

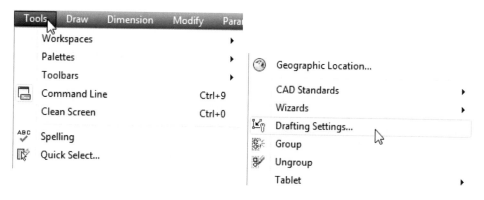

3. In the Drafting Settings dialog click on **Snap and Grid** and then under **Snap type** click on **Isometric Snap** (see image below)

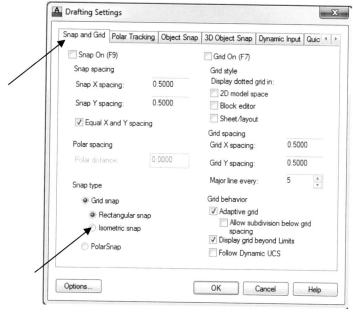

4. Click **OK**

11.2   STEPS IN CREATING ISOMETRIC AUTOCAD DRAWING

Once you have set the AutoCAD program to be in Isometric mode, you will notice that the cursor with the cross-hairs is at an angle based on the Isometric plane. There are 3 Isometric planes (Horizontal, Frontal and Profile) as explained in the Isometric Drawings title. To toggle between the three isometric planes hit **F5** (or **Ctrl e**) on the keyboard. To draw a line at 120˚ in isometric mode you MUST have your **ORTHO ON.**

11.3   STEPS IN CREATING A CUBE 1"×1"×1" AND AN ELLIPSE WITH .35" RADIUS IN EACH PROJECTION PLANE

1. Click on the **Line** command
2. Specify the **First point:** Click in the middle of the screen
3. Specify next point; type **1** and hit **Enter**
4. Specify next point; Move your cursor up, type **1** and hit **Enter** (see image below)

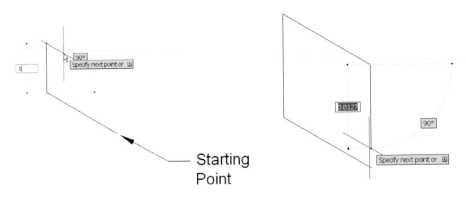

Starting
Point

5. Specify next point; Move your cursor to the right from the line you just finished; type **1** and hit **Enter**
6. Specify next point; move your cursor down; type **1** and hit **Enter**
7. Click on **Esc** on the keyboard

You have just created one of the 3 sides of the cube. This side is located in the frontal projection plane. To create the side in the Horizontal plane hit the **F5** key. Your cursor should be in the horizontal plane ready to create the second side of the cube.

8. Click on the **Line** command
9. Specify the First point: **Snap to the top left point of the line** (see image below)

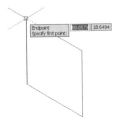

10. Specify next point; Move your cursor to the right; type **1** and hit **Enter**
11. Specify next point; Move your cursor to the right to form a side; type **1** and hit **Enter**
12. Specify next point; Move your cursor to the left; type **1** and hit **Enter**
13. Click on **Esc** – you should have an image like the one shown below

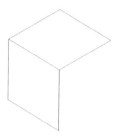

14. Click **F5** to switch to the Profile projection plane
15. Click on the **Line** command
16. Specify the first point: **Snap to the top right point of the line** (see image below)

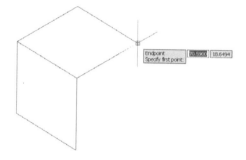

17. Specify next point; Move your cursor down; type **1** and hit **Enter**
18. Specify next point; Move your cursor to the left to form a side; type **1** and hit **Enter**
19. Click on **Esc** – you should have an image of a Cube like the one shown below

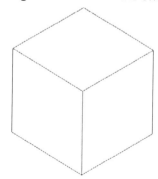

11.4   STEPS IN CREATING AN ISOMETRIC CIRCLE (ELLIPSE)

1. Select Horizontal Isometric plane by using the **F5** key
2. Turn your **Ortho OFF** and Draw a diagonal line as shown below

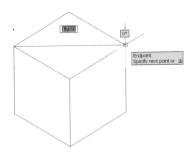

3. Click on the **Ellipse** button from the **Draw toolbar** (see image below)

4. Specify axis and point of ellipse or [Arc/Center/Isocircle]: type **I** (for Isocircle) and hit **Enter**
5. Specify center of Isocircle: **Snap to Midpoint of diagonal line** (see image below)

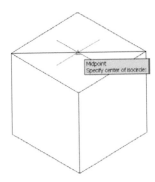

6. Specify radius of Isocircle [or Diameter]: type **.35** and hit **Enter** (see image on next page)

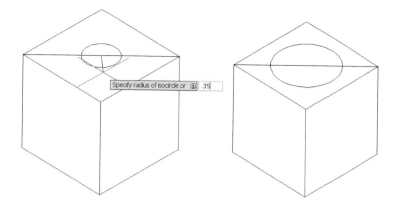

7. Click on **F5** key to select Profile isometric plane and repeat the steps 3 to 6 to create an Ellipse (Isocircle) in the Profile plane.

8. Click on **F5** key to select Frontal isometric plane and repeat the steps 3 to 6 to create an Ellipse (Isocircle) in the Frontal plane. Use diagonal construction lines in the Profile and Frontal planes to create the ellipses located exactly in the middle of the projection planes. Delete diagonal construction lines after ellipses are created. Your Cube with Ellipses in each plane should look like the image below.

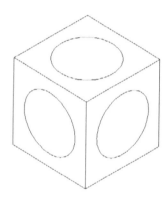

11.5   STEPS IN CREATING A CYLINDER (R=0.35" AND H=1") USING TANGENT TO QUADRANT COMMAND

1. Create a vertical centerline **1"** long (make sure your are in Frontal or Profile plane)
2. Click **F5** to switch to the Horizontal plane
3. Click on the **Ellipse button** from the **Draw toolbar**
4. Specify axis endpoint of ellipse or [Arc/Center/Isocircle]: type **I** and hit **Enter**
5. Specify Center of Isocircle: **Snap to Endpoint** of centerline (top endpoint of the line)
6. Specify radius of Isocircle [or Diameter]: type **0.35** and hit **Enter**

Repeat steps 3, 4, 5 (snap to lower point) and 6; you will have an image as shown below

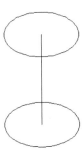

7. Click on **Line** command
8. Click on **Snap to Quadrant** button (see image below)

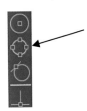

9. Bring your cursor close to the top Isocircle, then **Click when you see the diamond shape** (see image below)

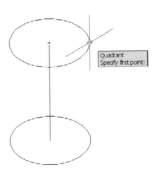

10. Click on **Snap to Quadrant** button **again** (do not miss this step)

11. Bring your cursor close to the bottom Isocircle, then **Click when you see the diamond shape** (see image below)

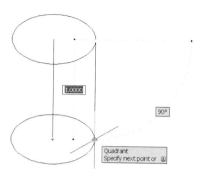

12. Repeat the steps 7, 8, 9, 10 and 11 on the other side to form a cylinder (see image below)

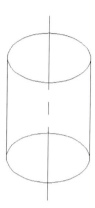

13. Change the line connecting the centers of the basis of the cylinder to Center Line (see image above) and trim the back portion of the ellipse of the bottom base (see image below)

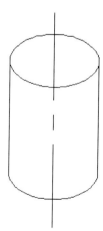

Chapter 12

DIMENSIONING

12.1 DIMENSIONING SYSTEMS

Dimensioning is a very important part of a drawing, showing all distances, angles, diameters and locations needed for making a part presented on a drawing. Each dimension consists of extension lines, dimension lines, and a number indicating the value of a specific dimension. Extension lines extend from the object line and are drawn perpendicular to dimension lines. There is a gap between the object line and extension line which is equivalent to the extension beyond the dimension line. Dimension lines are drawn parallel to the object line and should be about 10mm or ≈1/2" from the object line (see Fig 12.1.0).

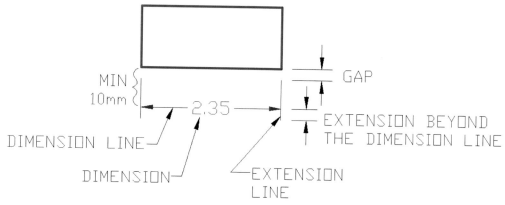

Fig.12.1.0

12.1.1 Linear Dimensioning

Linear dimensioning could be one of the following 3 types:

12.1.1 Chain-shows all dimensions as elements of a chain – see Fig. 12.1.1
12.1.2 Base Line-uses the same (base) extension line for all dimensions – see Fig. 12.1.2
12.1.3 Running-shows each dimension with a single arrow pointing to the next dimension – see Fig. 12.1.3

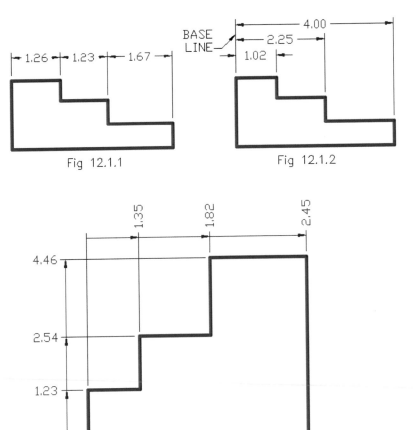

Fig 12.1.1   Fig 12.1.2

Fig 12.1.3

12.1.2 Angular Dimensioning

The value of the angle is normally shown in degrees (°) minutes (') and seconds (") -see Fig 12.2. The angle could also be shown in decimal degrees, which is an option that is not recommended because it requires conversion of the decimal portion into minutes and seconds when selecting an adequate measuring tool.

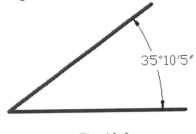

35°10'5"

Fig 12.2

12.1.3 Reference Dimensioning

Reference Dimensioning is used for checking purposes only and has to be indicated on a drawing either by putting a reference dimension in brackets or having suffix REF beside the dimension.

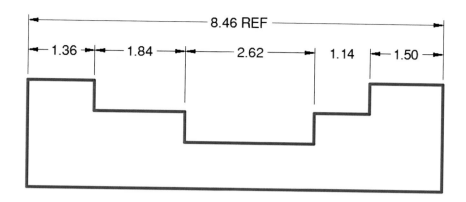

Fig 12.3

12.1.4 Tabular Dimensioning

Tabular Dimensioning is primarily used to show more than one different but similar shapes using one drawing and a table. Dimensions on the drawing are shown with letters and their values are indicated in a table that has to be shown close to the drawing (see Fig 12.4).

Tabular dimensioning is also used on a single part having many features by naming the features and placing their location and dimensions on a table. This is used when extension and dimension lines will be too complicated to read (see Fig 12.5).

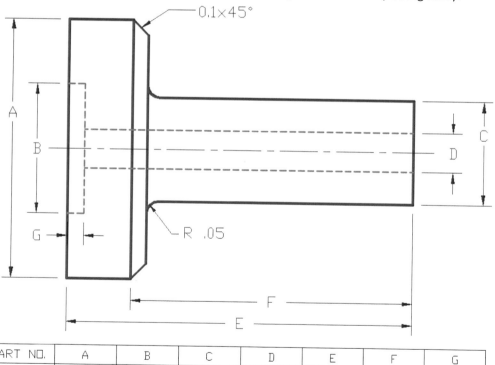

PART NO.	A	B	C	D	E	F	G
115-06	3.75	2.04	1.98	1.17	4.37	3.56	0.15
115-07	3.63	1.97	1.85	1.09	4.31	3.34	0.12
115-08	3.84	2.31	1.80	1.24	3.99	3.17	0.10

Fig 12.4

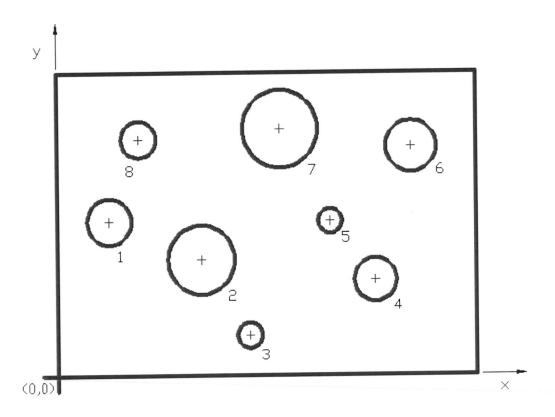

HOLE NO.	POSITION		SIZE
	X	Y	
1	1.154	3.104	⌀0.931
2	3.046	2.327	⌀1.392
3	4.055	0.801	⌀0.525
4	6.679	1.915	⌀.888
5	5.747	3.104	⌀0.491
6	7.422	4.603	⌀1.045
7	4.715	4.961	⌀1.576
8	1.722	4.768	⌀0.733

Fig 12.5

12.1.5 Arrowless Dimensioning

Arrowless Dimensioning uses one extension line with the value of the dimension shown above the extension line. No arrows or dimension lines are used; this makes the drawing clear and easy to read. The downside of this system is that some of the dimensions are vertical which requires rotating the drawing to read the dimension (see Fig 12.6).

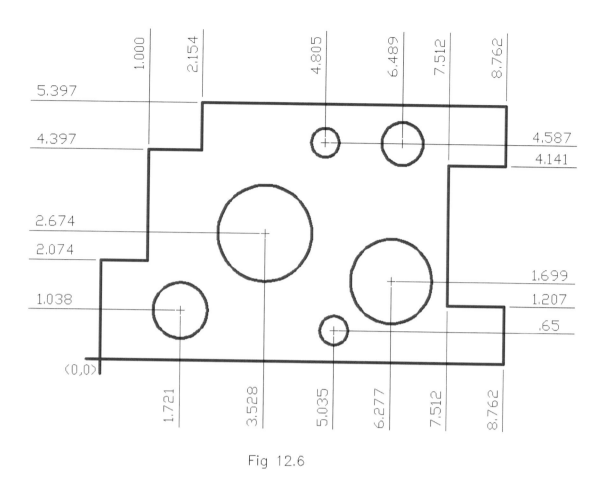

Fig 12.6

Considering the text (number) alignment with the dimension lines as a factor, there are 2 different dimensioning systems:

1. **Unidirectional dimensioning**: This shows all the dimensions in the same (horizontal) direction making the drawing easy to read.
2. **Aligned dimensioning**: This shows horizontal dimensions in a horizontal direction and vertical dimensions in a vertical direction. This system is more difficult to read, making it less practical than unidirectional dimensioning (see Fig 12.7).

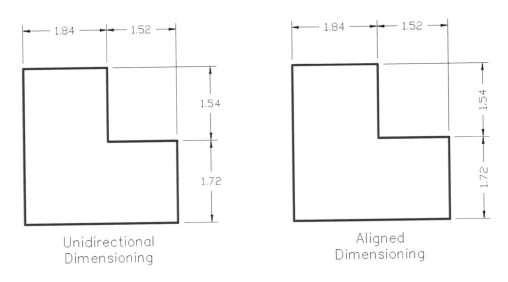

Unidirectional
Dimensioning

Aligned
Dimensioning

Fig 12.7

When more than one dimension line is drawn and base line dimensioning system is used, then the first dimension line has to be a minimum of 10mm from the object line and the other dimension lines should be separated a minimum of 6mm (see Fig. 12.8).

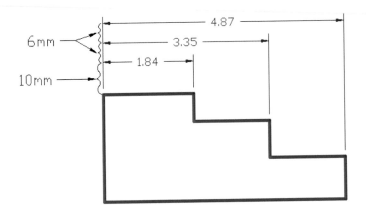

Fig 12.8

Chapter **13**

DIMENSIONING IN AUTOCAD

13.1 USING DIMENSION TOOLBAR

Before we start using any of the buttons from the dimension toolbar we have to select a dimension style. If we choose to use one of the newly created styles, we do not need to worry about the precision because it was already set when the new style was created. However, if we choose to use the standard dimension style we have to make sure we use correct precision (number of decimal points). If we use decimal inch measuring system in AutoCad Standard style by default, the precision is set to four decimal points. Sometimes this is not needed because the function of a specific part doesn't necessarily require such accurate manufacturing. If we don't select the appropriate precision, the production cost during manufacturing will unnecessarily increase.

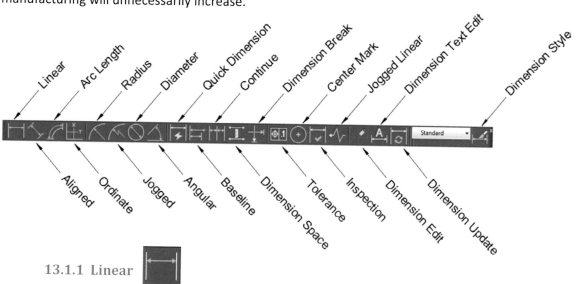

13.1.1 Linear

A linear dimension by definition is the measured distance between two points.

1. Click on **Linear** button
2. Specify first Extension line origin or <Select Object>. Click on first point (first extension line origin).
3. Specify second extension line origin: Click on the second point (see image on next page)
4. Specify dimension line location or [Mtext/Text/Angle/Horizontal/Vertical/Rotated]:
   Click on the desired position to put the text approximately 0.5" from the object line – see image below

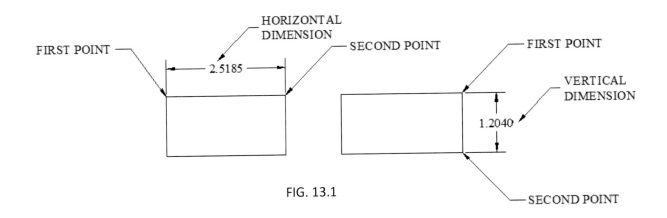

FIG. 13.1

5. The other options in using linear dimensions are shown on figure 13.1.1 and listed below:
   5.1. Mtext – option (2) – option (1) is by default and it is shown in fig. 13.1 above.
   5.2. Text – option (3)
   5.3. Angle – option (4) is used to put text at an angle other than 0° which is by default. In Fig 13.1.1 45° angle was used
   5.4. Horizontal – option (5) is used if there is a sloped line and we want to have the horizontal length of the slope.
   5.5. Vertical – option (6) – is used to put vertical dimensions of sloped line.
   5.6. Rotated – option (7) – is used if we want to put the dimension of the line seen at rotation angle (in Fig 13.1.1 rotation angle is 45°)

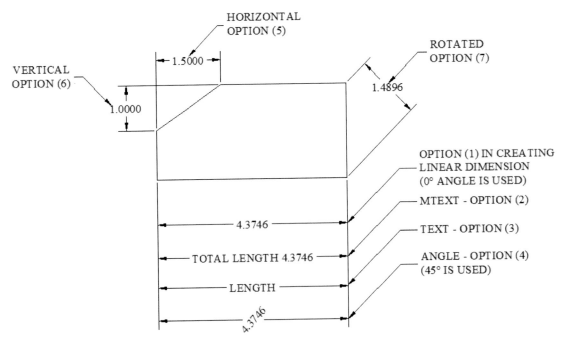

FIG. 13.1.1

109

13.1.2 Aligned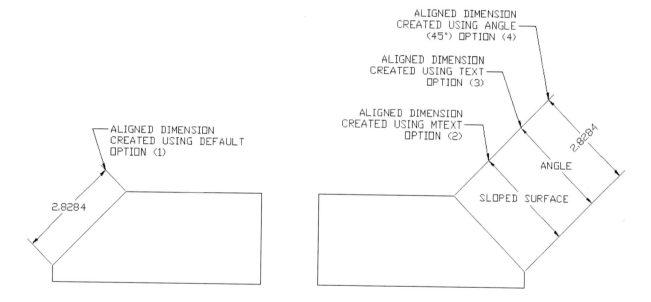

This function shows sloped linear dimension

1. Click on **Aligned** button
2. Specify first extension line origin or <select object>:
   Click on the first point of the slope.
3. Specify second extension line origin:
   Click on the second point of the slope
4. Specify dimension line location or [Mtext/Text/Angle]:
   Click about 0.5" from the sloped line.
5. Putting aligned dimension (option 1) and the other options in using align dimension are shown in Fig. 13.2 and listed below:
   5.1. Mtext – option (2)
   5.2. Text – option (3)
   5.3. Angle – (45° is used) – option (4)

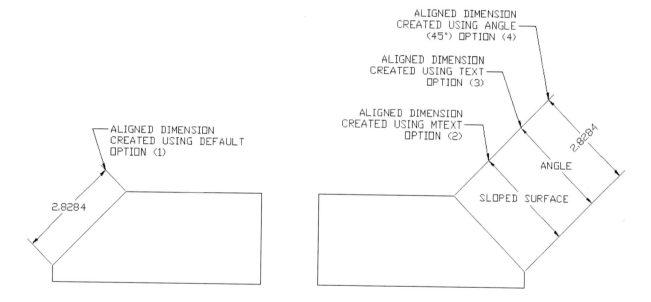

FIG. 13.2

13.1.3 Arc Length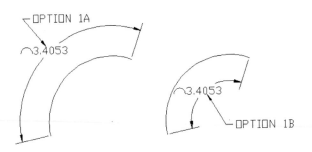

This function shows the dimension of an arc. There are 3 options in terms of showing arc length symbol (please see item 3.5.4 – of section 13.2 in this chapter)

1. Create an arc (any size)
2. Click on Arc Length button
3. Select arc or polyline arc segment:
   Click on **Arc**
4. Specify Arc Length dimension location or [Mtext/Text/Angle/Partial/Leader]:
5. Click in desired position to locate arc length dimension. The position could be outside (1A) or inside (1B) the arc – see 13.3.1 below

FIG. 13.3.1

6. The other options in using Arc Length dimension are shown in Fig. 13.3.2 and used below:
   6.1. Mtext – option (2)
   6.2. Text – option (3)
   6.3. Angle – (45° is used) option (4)
   6.4. Partial – option (5)
   6.5. Leader – option (6)

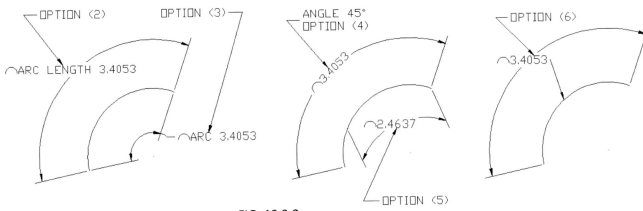

FIG. 13.3.2

13.1.4 Ordinate (Arrowless) Dimensioning

1. This type of dimensioning is very practical because it has no arrows or dimension lines, there are only extension lines and the dimension – see Fig. 13.4.1

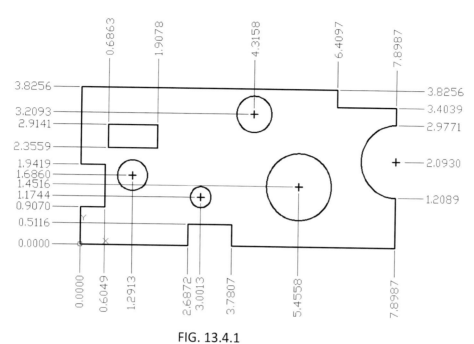

FIG. 13.4.1

The downside of this dimensioning system is the dimensions are aligned with the extension lines which make reading the numbers more difficult than if they were horizontal. The other disadvantage of this ordinate dimensioning is that when dimensions are close to each other it may be difficult to focus on a specific dimension. This problem could be solved by placing the dimension in a staggered position – see Fig. 13.4.2

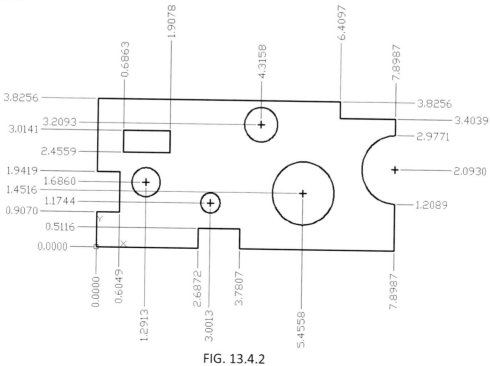

FIG. 13.4.2

The other options in using Ordinate Dimensioning are shown below.

2. X Datum – shows dimensions in X- direction measured from a datum point (0,0) see Fig. 13.4.2.2 below.

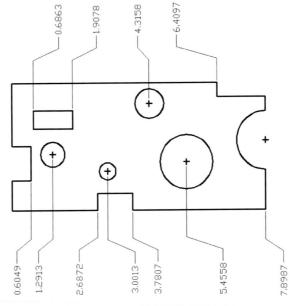

FIG. 13.4.2.2

3. Y Datum – shows dimensions in Y – direction measured from a datum point (0,0) see Fig. 14.4.2.3 below

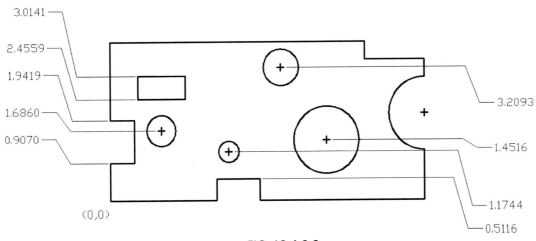

FIG. 13.4.2.3

113

4. Mtext – Function is used if we want to have a multiple line text (with or without dimensions) to be shown – see Fig. 13.4.2.4 below

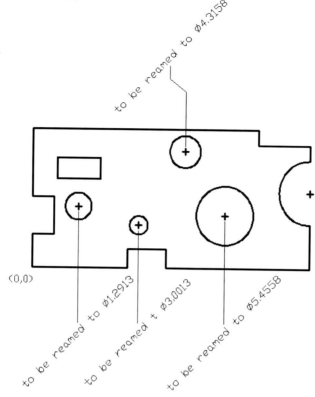

FIG. 13.4.2.4

5. Text – option is used to put a text (with or without dimensions) – see Fig. 13.4.2.5 below

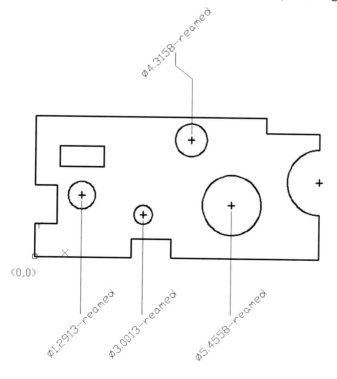

FIG. 13.4.2.5

6. Angle – Option is used to partially or fully solve the problem of dimensions that are placed in vertical position. By using angle (ex: 45°) option we can make the numbers more easily readable without rotating the drawing – see Fig. 13.4.2.6 below

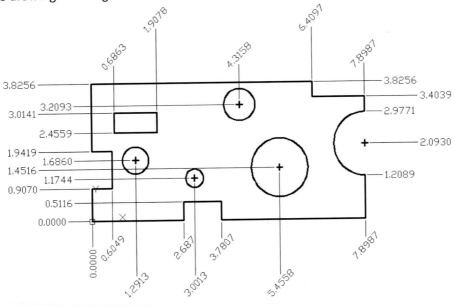

FIG. 13.4.2.6

13.1.5 Radius

This is one of the most commonly used commands from the dimension toolbar.

1. Create any size circle
2. Click on the radius button
3. Select arc or circle: Click on the circle
4. Specify dimension line location or [Mtext/Text/Angle]:
    Click in the position you want dimension to be located.
    Repeat the steps 1 to 4 on an arc. As you can see the dimension can be located outside or inside at any point – see option (1) Fig. 13.5

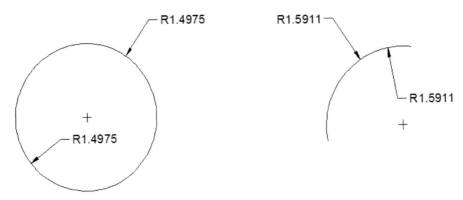

FIG. 13.5

5. The other option in using radius dimension are shown in Fig. 13.5.1 and listed below:
    5.1. Mtext – option (2)
    5.2. Text – option (3)
    5.3. Angle – option (4)
        Specify angle of dimension text: type **45°** and hit **ENTER**.
        Specify dimension line location

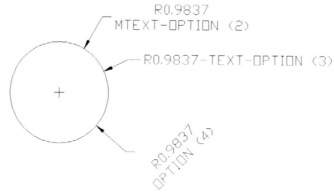

FIG. 13.5.1

13.1.6 Jogged Dimensioning

This type of Dimensioning is equally used in manual and CAD dimensioning when the radius of an arc is very big and the center of the arc is outside of the drafting area. By using this system, an operator who is going to manufacture the part is aware about the above mentioned facts. Jog angle by default is 45°, although when creating a new dimension style we can choose a different value.

1. Create a large arc
2. Click on jogged button
3. Select Arc or Circle: click on the arc
4. Specify center location override: Click on desired center location
5. Specify dimension line location or [Mtext/Text/Angle]: Click in the desired dimension line location
6. Specify jog location: Click in the desired jog location – option (1)
7. Option (2) – Mtext: repeat steps 3 and 4
8. In step 5: type MT and hit ENTER. You will see multiple text dialog box. Type desired text (ex: Mtext) and O.K.
9. Option (3) – Text. Same as previous option except you don't have multiline text.
10. Option (4) – Angle
    Do steps 1, 2, 3, and in step 4 type: **A** and hit **ENTER**.
    Specify angle of Dimension text: type 45 and hit ENTER.
    Specify desired dimension line location
    Specify jog location: Specify (Click in desired jog location)

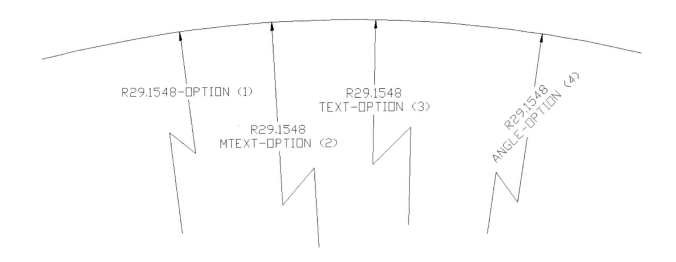

FIG. 13.6

13.1.7 Diameter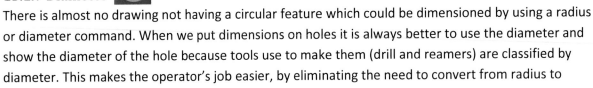

There is almost no drawing not having a circular feature which could be dimensioned by using a radius or diameter command. When we put dimensions on holes it is always better to use the diameter and show the diameter of the hole because tools use to make them (drill and reamers) are classified by diameter. This makes the operator's job easier, by eliminating the need to convert from radius to diameter.

1. Create any size circle
2. Click on Diameter button
3. Select arc or circle
4. Specify dimension line location or [Mtext/Text/Angle/]: Click in the position that you want the diameter dimension to be located.
   Repeat the steps 1 to 4 on an arc, and note that the dimension (diameter) could be located outside or inside at any point – option (1) see Fig. 13.7

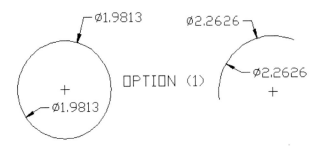

FIG. 13.7

5. The other options in using diameter dimensions are shown in Fig. 13.7.1 and listed below:
   5.1. Mtext – option (2)
   5.2. Text – option (3)
   5.3. Angle – option (4)

117

Specify angle of dimension text: type 45° and hit ENTER
Specify dimension line location

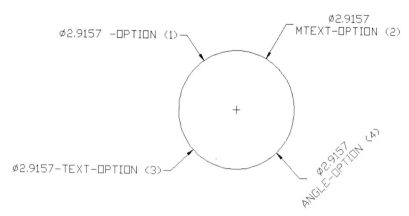

FIG. 13.7.1

13.1.8 Angular

There are many drawings having a sloped surface or other features that need to be dimensioned using the angular function.

The most common case is when angular dimension needs to be put on the sloped surface.

To put angular dimension on sloped surface: - see Fig. 13.8 on the next page:

1. Click on angular dimension symbol
2. Select arc, circle, line or <specify vertex>:
       Click on line 1
3. Select second line: - Click on line 2
4. Specify dimension arc location or [Mtext/Text/Angle/Quadrant]:
       Click in the desired position – option (1a) on the left side of the drawing. Notice that the same angle 31°, - option (1a) could be placed close to line 2
       You notice that in continuation of 31° angle – option (1a) there is another angle 149° which is also obtained by clicking on line (1) and line (2). These pair of angles 31° and 149° add up to 180° (option 1a) the other supplementary pair is 59° and 121° - shown in option (1b) in order to show 59° or 121° angle we need to click on line (1) and line (3) see Fig. 13.8

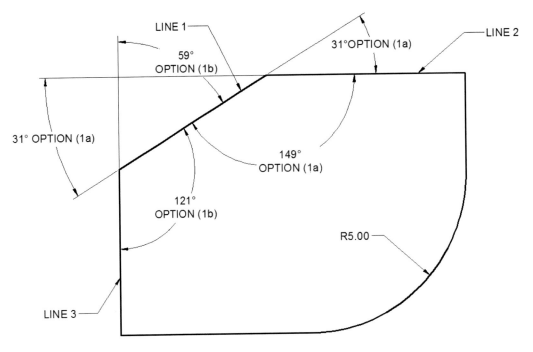

FIG. 13.8

5. The other options in using angular dimensions are shown below:
   5.1. Dimensioning an arc – option (2) – see Fig. 13.8.1

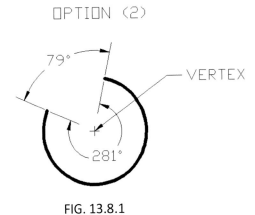

FIG. 13.8.1

   5.2. Dimensioning an angle between a specific point 1 a circle, and a second angle endpoint -2. See Fig. 13.8.2

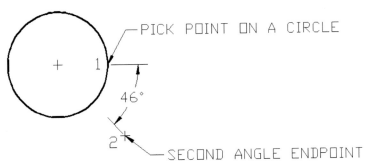

FIG. 13.8.2

5.3. Dimensioning an angle between 2 points (point 1 and 2) using vertex as a reference center point – see Fig. 13.8.3

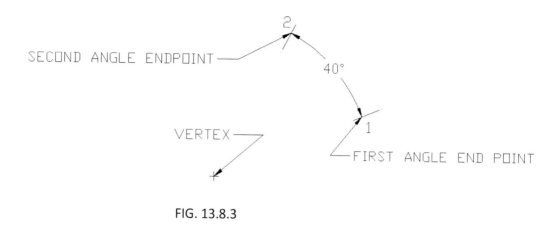

FIG. 13.8.3

13.1.9 Quick Dimensioning

If the slope of the object is suitable for quick dimensioning, which is basically chain dimensioning, we can use this option and save some time compared to using a continue (chain) button.

Using Quick Dimensioning is very simple and very quick. In order to use this function:

1. Create an object as shown in Fig. 13.9.1 – step 1 below

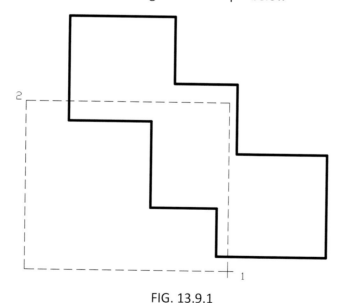

FIG. 13.9.1

2. Click on Quick Dimensioning   button
3. Select geometry: use a window option from the lower right (point 1) to the top left corner (point 2) as shown in Fig. 13.9.1 and hit ENTER.

4. Specify dimension line position as shown in Fig. 13.9.1a. repeat steps 3 and 4 and the object will be completely dimensioned in a vertical position – see Fig. 13.9.1b

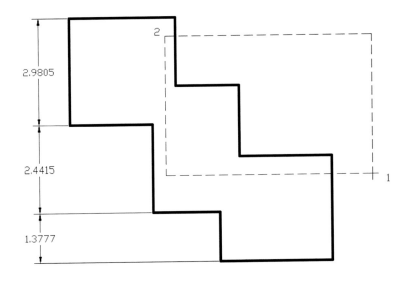

FIG. 13.9.1a

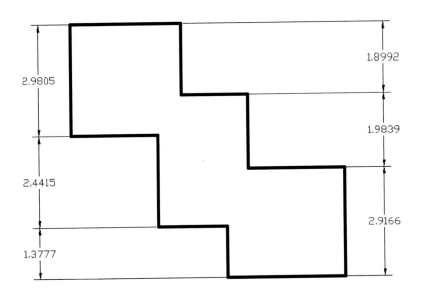

FIG. 13.9.1b

5. Repeat the steps 2,3, and 4 twice (at the top and bottom part of the object) and you will have the object horizontally dimensioned very quickly – see Fig. 13.9.1c

121

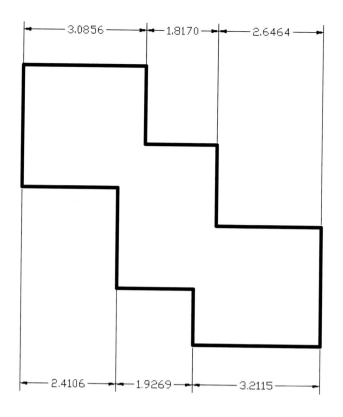

FIG. 13.9.1c

13.1.10 Baseline Dimensioning

This type of dimensioning is extensively used to avoid so called tolerance accumulation. Every single dimension, horizontal or vertical, is taken from the same extension line, respectively, called the base line.

1. To use the baseline dimensioning button we need to use the linear dimensioning button and create the first dimension 1.1517 using points 1 and 2 – see Fig. 13.10 A
2. Click on baseline dimension button and specify the second point (click on point 2) to create 2.2604 and the other (called second again because the baseline is the first extension line for all dimensions) – click on point 3 to create 2.9082 dimension – see Fig. 13.10 B

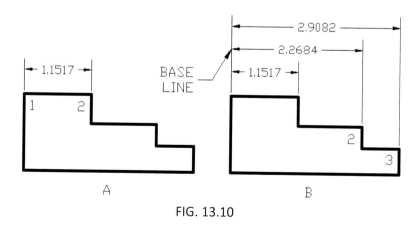

FIG. 13.10

13.1.11 Continue (Chain) Dimensioning

A very practical method and used extensively on drawings when no tolerance is shown.

1. Create a shape (A)
2. Click on the linear dimension button and after specifying first point 1 and second point 2 specify the desired position for the first dimension – see Fig. 13.11-A
3. Click on the continue button and the points 2 and 3 in Fig. 14.11-B so that all the steps will be dimensioned using continue (Chain) Dimensioning system. – See Fig. 13.11-B below

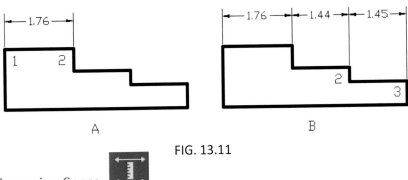

FIG. 13.11

13.12 Dimension Space

On the part shown below if we want the second dimension (1.501) to be aligned with the first one (2.022) as not to have any dimension space between them use the following steps:

1. Click on Dimension Space button
2. Select base dimension (2.022)
   Click on point 1
3. Select Dimensions to space:
   Click on point 2 and hit ENTER
   See Fig 13.12.1-A below
4. Enter the value or <Auto>: type 0 and hit ENTER – See Fig. 13.12.1-B below

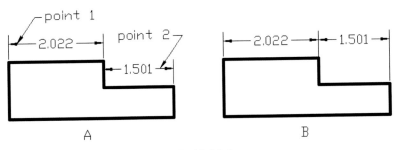

FIG. 13.12.1

If we have an object with (for example) 3 dimensions and 2 of them (2.908 and 4.059) are not equally spaced, we can make the distance between them equal by moving 2.908 half way between the 1.686 and 4.059 dimensions. We have to find out the distance between them first (it is 1.0730) and move the 2.908 dimension half of 1.073 (which is 0.536) away from each of the other two dimensions. See Fig. 13.12.2-A

1. Click on dimension space button
2. Select both dimensions: click on Dimension 1
3. Select dimensions to space: click on dimensions 2 and 3 and hit ENTER
4. Select dimensions to space: Hit ENTER
5. Enter value or <Auto>: type 0.536

   You will notice dimension 2.908 moving equidistant to the other two dimensions – see Fig. 13.12.2-B
6. Repeat steps 1 to 5 and instead of typing 0.536 Hit ENTER. The dimensions will be spaced as shown in Fig. 13.12.2-C

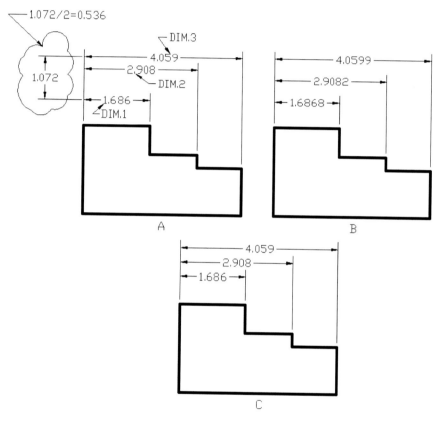

FIG. 13.12.2

13.13 Dimension Break

When a dimension crosses an object or the extension line is crossing or is very close to an arrow, we use dimension break to break a dimension or extension line.

1. Click on dimension break button
2. Select dimension to add/remove break or [multiple]: click on 2.02 dimension (step 1)
3. Select object to break dimension [   ] <Auto>: click on vertical line (step 2) notice that there is a break (dimension break) on the extension line. – Fig. 13.13

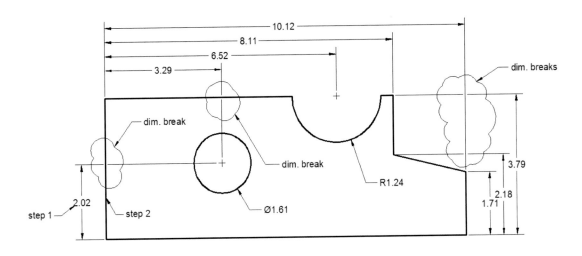

FIG. 13.13

13.1.14 Tolerance

This button is used to put GD&T (Geometric Dimension and Tolerance) on a drawing. This is a very important function and only the methods required to produce the symbols and an explanation of them will be given. GD&T includes a vast amount of information and is typically taught as a separate subject.

There are standard geometric symbols that are listed below.

STANDARD GEOMETRIC SYMBOLS					
TYPE OF TOLERANCE	CHARACTERISTIC	SYMBOL	TYPE OF TOLERANCE	CHARACTERISTIC	SYMBOL
FORM	STRAIGHTNESS	—	ORIENTATION	ANGULARITY	∠
	FLATNESS	▱		PERPENDICULARITY	⊥
	CIRCULARITY	○		PARALLELISM	//
	CYLINDRICITY	⌭	LOCATION	POSITION	⊕
PROFILE	PROFILE OF A LINE	⌒		CONCENTRICITY	◎
	PROFILE OF A SURFACE	⌓		SYMMETRY	⌯
			RUNOUT	CIRCULAR RUNOUT	↗
				TOTAL RUNOUT	⌰

FIG. 13.14.1

125

The basic terms used in GD&T are shown on the drawing below.

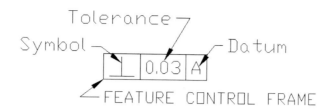

FIG. 13.14.2

To put some GD&T feature (we will do this 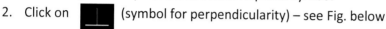 first) click on the tolerance  button.

1. Click on sym back quadrant to select required symbol
2. Click on (symbol for perpendicularity) – see Fig. below

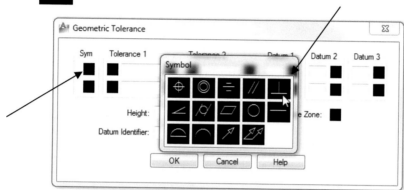

FIG. 13.14.3

3. In the space for tolerance 1 type 0.03
4. In the space for datum 1 type A
   Then click **OK**
5. Click in the desired position to put the feature frame (GD&T) – see below

To create the following feature frame :   ⊕ | ⌀0.05Ⓜ | A

1. Click on the tolerance button and then click on sym quadrant –step 1, and select symbol – step 2

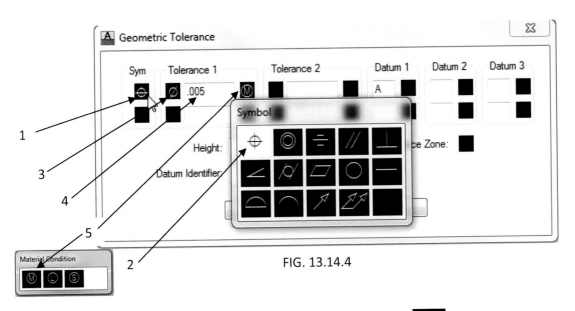

FIG. 13.14.4

2. Do steps 3 and 4 (click Ø and type 0.05). In step 5 click on (meaning maximum material condition) and in step 6 type: **A** then click **OK** – see Fig. 13.14.4

Note: By default a leader line is annotated to MText and if you would like a leader line annotated to GD&T and draw this GD&T feature frame
we have to modify the following settings first.

1. On the command line type: **qleader** and Hit **ENTER**
2. Specify first leader point or <settings>: Hit **ENTER** again

You will see leader settings dialog box shown below:

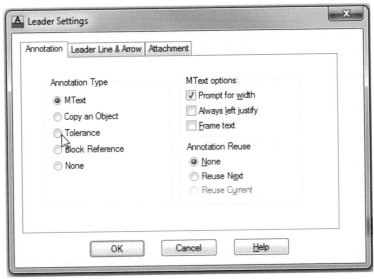

3. Click on Tolerance and **OK**

4. Specify first leader point or <settings>: click in the position for first point (point 1)
5. Specify next point: click in the desired position (point 2)
6. Specify next point: click in the desired position (point 3): Geometric Tolerance dialog box will pop-up.
7. In the first row for Tolerance 1 – type **B**, then move to the second row and do the rest as explained before typing **B** in datum 2 space and click **OK** you will see the GD&T feature frame with a leader line as shown below. – Fig. 13.14.6

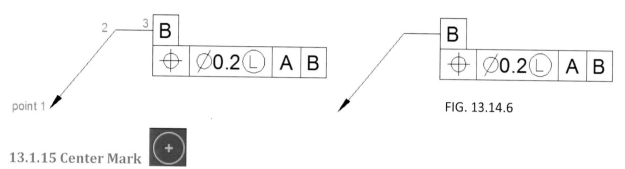

FIG. 13.14.6

13.1.15 Center Mark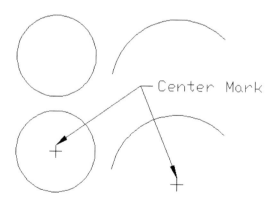

When we create circles or arcs they don't have a center mark, unless we use our dimension style in which we have to specify (see item 3.5.2 in section 13.2 of this chapter)

If the circles or arcs are without center marks we can insert them using the following steps.

1. Create a circle and an arc as shown below.
2. Click on the center mark button.
3. Select arc or circle: click on the circle and you will see the center mark
4. Repeat step 3 on the arc. – see Fig 13.15 below.

FIG. 13.15

13.1.16 Inspection

In the process of manufacturing we often check the dimensions of a part to be certain the value is correct. If there are tolerances we check if the parts are within tolerance limits. The frequency in which we perform these tasks is specified by the inspection function.

1. Create the part with the dimensions as shown below.

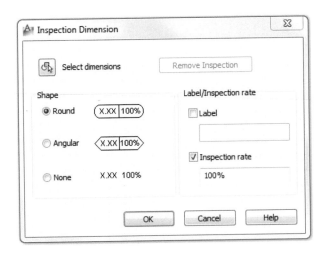

FIG. 13.16.1

2. Click on the inspection button. Inspection dimension dialog box will pop-up see Fig. 13.16.2

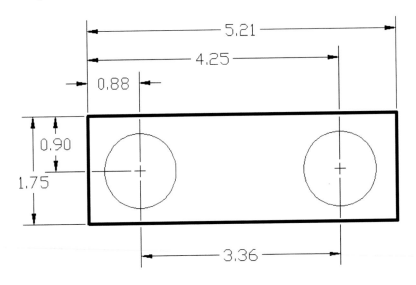

3. Select shape of the inspection form (round, angular or none) specify the inspection rate (ex: 50% or 100%) and click on   select the dimension button.
4. Select dimensions: ex 3.36 – 100% and hit **ENTER** – Inspection Dimension will pop-up.
5. Click **OK** in the Inspection Dimension dialog box.

6. Repeat steps 2 to 5 selecting round inspection form and 50% inspection rate – see Fig. 13.16.3

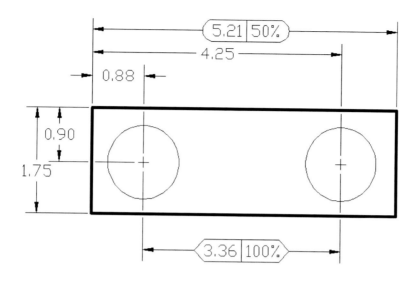

FIG. 13.16.3

13.1.17 Jogged Linear

If we want to draw a very long part in full scale and plot it on a small size paper we can use full section and jogged linear dimension.

1. Create the part with jogged lines representing the part is broken (or shortened).
2. Click on jogged linear button.
3. Select dimension to add jog or [Remove]: click on 16.6
4. Specify a location: click on snap to midpoint and click on the midpoint of the dimension line (1).
   – see Fig. 13.17 below

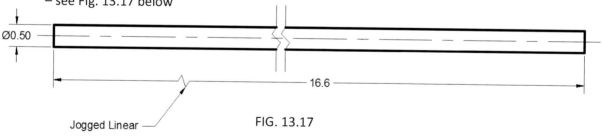

Jogged Linear ———⟋   FIG. 13.17

13.1.18 Dimension Edit

This function can rotate, modify or change the oblique angle on text or extension lines.

1. Create 5.81x1.59 rectangle as shown on next page.
2. Click on the Dimension Edit button.
3. Enter type of dimension editing: type **H** (for Home) and Hit **ENTER**
4. Select object: click on the staggered Dimension and Hit **ENTER**. The dimension will move to its previous position

5. Click on DIMENSION EDIT
6. Edit type of dimension editing: type R (for Text Rotation Angle).
7. Specify angle for dimension Text: type **45** and Hit **ENTER**.
8. Select dimension: (see Text Rotation option)
9. The *New* option allows us to edit the value of the text – (1.59 – old   1.77 – new) – see Fig. 13.18
   with all options

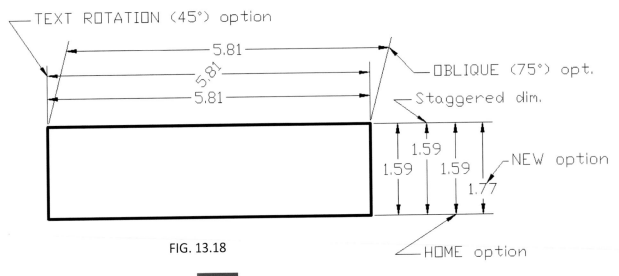

FIG. 13.18

13.1.19 Dimension Text Edit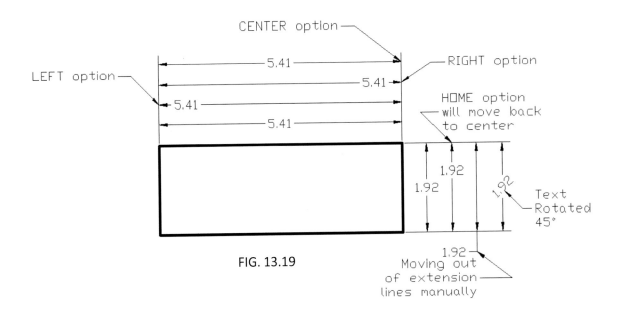
Create 5.41x1.92 rectangle

1. Click on the Dimension Text Edit button and follow the options available – see Fig. 13.19

FIG. 13.19

13.1.20 Dimension Update

This function is used when we have previously used another dimension style 1 and we want dimensions created using the previous style 1 to be converted – updated using the new dimension style 2.

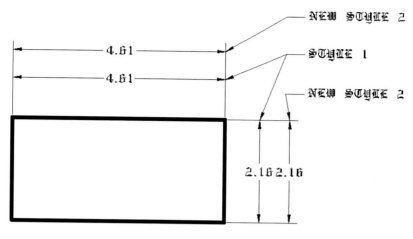

FIG. 13.20

13.2 DIMENSIONING STYLE

In AutoCAD there is a standard Dimension Style which can be used to put dimensions on a drawing without any settings, but if we want to have a new Dimension Style with specific characteristics we have to create a new style following the steps described below.

1. Click on **Dimension Style** Manager button (see image below)

Dimension Style

2. The meaning of the functions in the **Dimension Style Manager dialog box** are as follows:

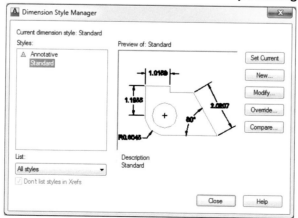

2.1 **Set Current** is used to set a previously selected style to become Current. To select and make a specific style instantly current, **Click** on Dim Style Control button and select your style (see image below).

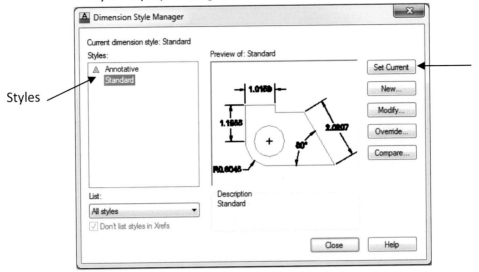

2.2 **New** button is used to create a New Style – it will be explained in detail later

2.3 **Modify** button is used to change a style. Whatever changes we make in this style will automatically affect/change all dimensions created using the modified style.

2.4 **Override** button is used when we want to create some dimensions with different settings without affecting dimensions already created with another style.

2.5 **Compare** button is used to compare 2 different styles.

3. **CREATE A NEW DIMENSION STYLE**

3.1 In Dimension Style Manager dialog box, click on **New** and type a name that will associate with the type of drawing you will create. Ex: Mechanical (see image below)

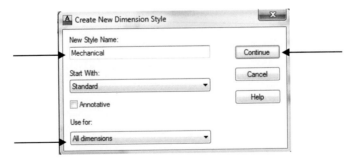

3.2 Use for **All dimensions** (keep this option so that this Style will be applied to all dimensions)

3.3 Click on **Continue**

3.4 **LINES**

3.4.1 **Dimension lines** – keep the following settings:
- Color: ☐ ByBlock

- Linetype: – ByBlock
- Lineweight: – ByBlock
- **Extend beyond ticks: 0.125** is active only if we select Architectural tick for arrowheads from Symbols and Arrows toolbar (see image below)

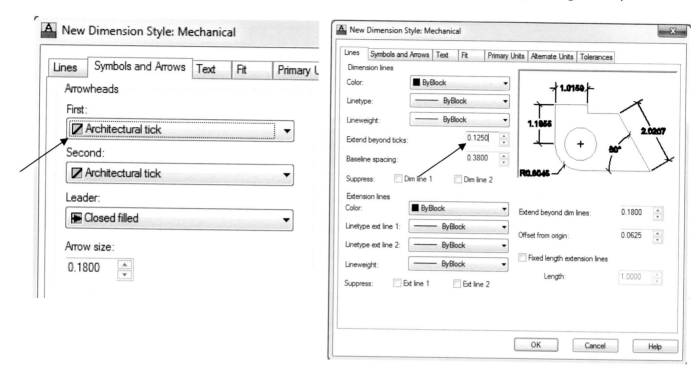

There is a standard that applies to the Extend beyond the ticks (or arrows) value as well as the value of the gap (known as OFFSET FROM ORIGIN) between the extension lines and object line shown below. These values are variable based on the size of the drawing.

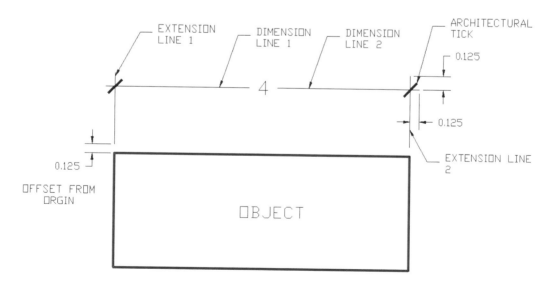

- **Baseline spacing: 0.380** – (keep this standard value)
- **Suppress:** ☐ Dim line 1 ☐ Dim line 2 is used when we want to have one or both dimension lines suppressed (see following image)

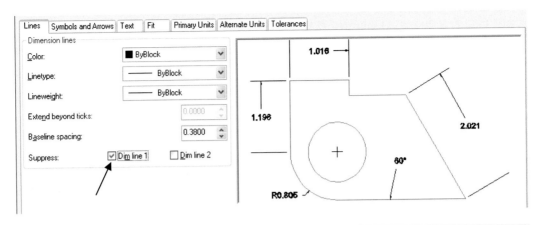

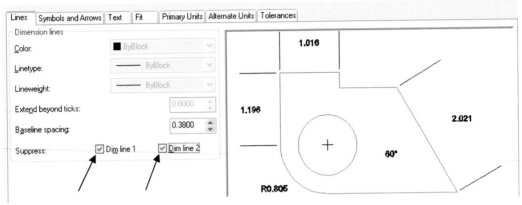

3.4.2 **Extension lines** – keep the following settings:

- Color: ☐ **ByBlock**
- Linetype ext line 1: – ByBlock
- Linetype ext line 2: – ByBlock
- Lineweight: – ByBlock
- Suppress: ☐ Ext line 1 ☐ Ext line 2 is used when we want to have one or both extension lines suppressed
- Extend beyond dim lines: **0.125**
- Offset from Origin: **0.125**
- ☐ **Fixed length extension lines**, if selected to be active, will allow us to set the Length of the extension lines
- **Length:** 1.000 or bigger based on the size of the drawing

3.5 **SYMBOLS AND ARROWS** (See Image of Symbols and Arrows Toolbar on previous page)

3.5.1 **Arrowheads**

- First: →**Closed filled** option is normally used for mechanical drawings. From the drop down list we can select another type of arrowhead.
- Second: →**Closed filled** (normally the second arrowhead is the same as the First one)

135

- Leader: →**Closed filled** or any other from the drop down list
- **Arrow size: 0.180** by default. **Note: The arrow size has to be equal to the text height.** If we change the arrow size we have to change the text height in the text toolbar.

3.5.2 **Center marks** are used to locate the center when drawing a circle. There are 3 options in identifying the center of a circle:
- **None** – do not locate the center
- **Mark:** 0.090 (by default) – have a little mark to locate the center. Note that the size of the mark could be increased or reduced by clicking on the arrows beside the number representing the length of the mark.
- **Line** – have center lines

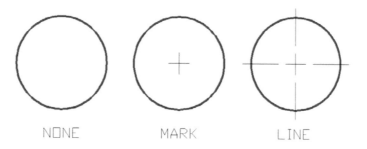

3.5.3 **Dimension Break**
- **Break size**: specifies the gap created for dimensions

3.5.4 **Arc Length Symbol** is used when dimensioning an arc. There are 3 options when dimensioning an arc:
- **Preceding dimension text** will put an arc symbol before the value
- **Above dimension text** will put an arc symbol above the value
- **None** will not put an arc symbol

3.5.5 **Radius Jog Dimension**. Jog Dimensioning is used to indicate that the length of the radius is shortened when a radius of an arc is too long and the center is too far from an arc.
- **Jog Angle: 45°** – by default. The value of this angle could be from 5° to 90° (see image below)

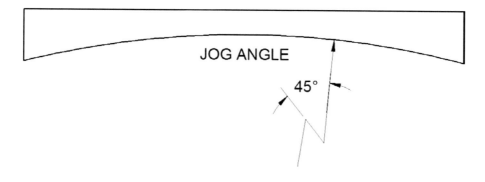

3.5.6 **Linear Jog Dimension** is used to indicate that a dimension line is shortened.

- **Jog Height factor: 1.5 x text height**. The Jog Height by default is 1.5 higher than the Text.

3.6 TEXT

The Text dialog box shows Text appearance, Text placement and Text alignment.

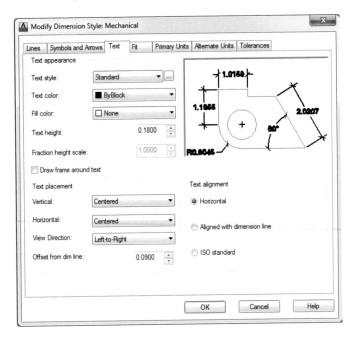

3.6.1 **Text appearance**

- Text style: **Standard** style is by default.
  From drop list we can select another style that we have previously created.
- Text color: ☐ **ByBlock**
- Fill color: ☐ **None** From drop list we can select one of the colors listed
- Text height: **0.180** is by default. **Make sure text height is equivalent to the Arrow size.**
- Fraction height scale: **1.0000** means that the height of numbers in the fraction is same as the height of the whole numbers. This function is available only when Fractional Unit format is selected in Primary units.
- ☐ **Draw frame around text** if checked ☑ it will draw a box around the text.

3.6.2 **Text placement**

- Vertical: **Centered** places the text at the center of the dimension lines, **Above** places the text above the dimension line, **Outside** places the text on the side of the dimension, **JIS** places the text above the dimension line according to the Japanese Industrial Standard.

137

- Horizontal: **Centered** places the text at the center of the dimension lines, **At Ext Line 1** justifies the text to the first extension line, **At Ext Line 2** justifies the text to the second extension line, **Over Ext Line 1** places the text over the first extension line, **Over Ext Line 2** places the text over the second extension line.
- **Offset from Dim Line**: Sets the gap between the text and the dimension lines.

3.6.3 Text Alignment

- **Horizontal** places the text in a horizontal position known as **Unidirectional** dimensioning.
- **Aligned with Dimension Line** aligns the text with the dimension line which is also known as **Aligned** Dimensioning
- **ISO** places the text in Horizontal position when the text is outside the extension lines and Aligns the text when it fits between the extension lines.

3.7 FIT

The Fit tab shows the options of placing the text under different circumstances.

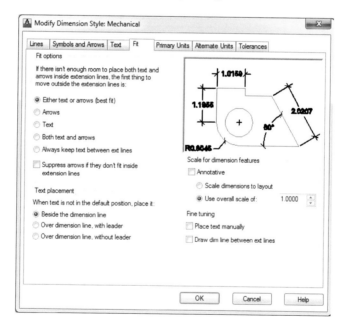

3.7.1 Fit Options give possible placements for the text and arrows. If there is not enough room to place both the text and arrows inside the extension lines, the first thing to move outside the extension lines is:

- **Either the text or the arrows (best fit)** is the first option (also default option) and is considered the best option. The other options are:
- **Arrows** to be moved outside first

- **Text** to be moved outside first

- **Both Text and Arrows** to be moved outside

- **Always keep text between text lines** keeps the text between the extension lines
- **Suppress arrows if they don't fit inside the extension lines** option will show no arrowheads

3.7.2 Text Placement

When the text is not in a default position there are 3 options available:

- **Beside the dimension line**

- **Over dimension line, with leader**

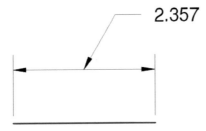

- **Over dimension line, without leader**

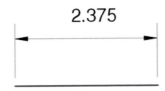

3.7.3   Scale for Dimension Features

- **Scale dimensions to layout** scales dimensions between model space and layout using a scale factor
- **Use overall scale of: 1.000** makes text and arrows the same size. To make the text and arrows twice as big at the same time we need to increase the scale to 2. To make them half of their size we need to scale to 0.5.

3.7.4   Fine Tuning

- **Place text manually:** this option makes it possible to manually put the text in a desired position in order to have so called **Staggered dimensioning**, (see image below) which is used to better focus on dimensions.

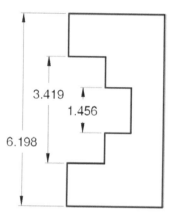

3.8 **PRIMARY UNITS** (see image below).

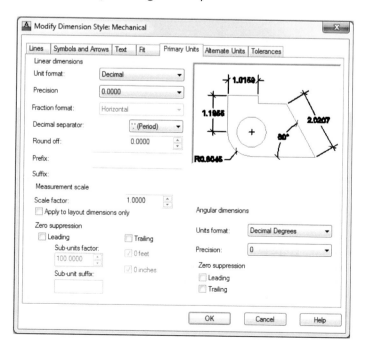

3.8.1 Linear dimensions

- **Unit format** sets one of the five options (click on the Drop-down arrow to see and select one) for types of units available.
- **Precision** sets the number of decimal places as required precision for linear dimension.
  It is very important not to specify more decimal places than needed; otherwise it will increase the requirements for a more accurate manufacturing process to be used, which will eventually increase the cost.
- **Fraction format**: is available only when Fractional units are selected. This format shows one of the 3 options (Horizontal $1\frac{3}{16}$; Diagonal $1\ ^3\!/_{16}$; Not Stacked 1 3/16) of how the fractions will be shown on the drawing (see image below).

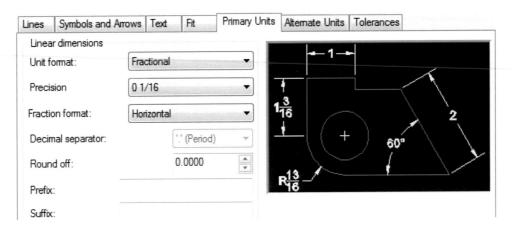

- **Decimal separator**: could be a Comma, Period or Space and it is used to separate the decimal portion from the whole number.
- **Round off**: is used to specify how to round off decimals or fractions.
- **Prefix**: is used to write text or a symbol before the dimension.
- **Suffix**: is used to write text or a symbol after the dimension.

3.8.2 Measurement scale

- **Scale factor**: is used to scale a dimension. For example, a scale factor 2 will make a dimension twice as big as the actual size.
- **Apply to layout dimensions only**: if checked, will apply the Scale factor to Layout mode.

3.8.3 Zero suppression

- **Leading**: if checked will eliminate the leading zeros in a linear dimension.
- **Trailing**: if checked will eliminate the zeros after a decimal point.

3.8.4 Angular dimensions

- **Units format**: from the four options available, the second one (**Degrees Minutes Seconds**) is the most practical from a machinist's point of view in terms of selecting a measuring tool and without doing any converting.
- **Precision**: sets the number of decimal places as required precision for angular dimension.

3.8.5 Zero suppression
- **Leading**: if checked will eliminate the leading zeros of angular dimensions.
- **Trailing**: if checked will eliminate the zeros after a decimal point

3.9 ALTERNATE UNITS (see image below).

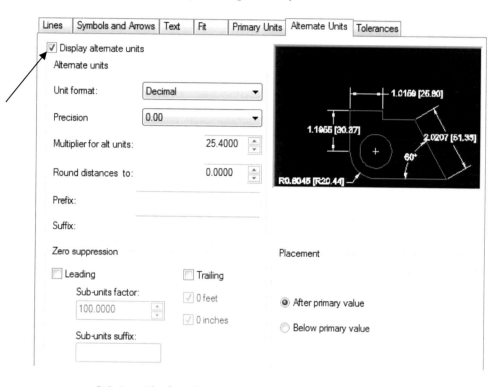

3.9.1 Display alternate units:
- If checked will display alternate units. If inches are selected as Primary units then Alternate units will be millimeters and vice versa. This feature is very practical, especially in cases where a drawing might be used in companies that use both systems equally. Could also be used in two different companies, one using inch and the other metric.

3.9.2 Alternate units
- **Unit format**: sets one of several options for types of units available.
- **Precision**: sets the number of decimal places as required precision for alternate units for linear dimension.
- **Multiplier for alt units**: 25.4 is the conversion factor for inches to millimeters (1" = 25.4 mm).
- **Round distances to**: if set at 0.000 – no rounding is used.

- **Prefix**: is used to write text or a symbol before the alternate dimension.
- **Suffix**: is used to write text or a symbol after the alternate dimension.

3.9.3 Zero suppression
- **Leading**: if checked will eliminate the leading zeros in a linear alternate dimension.
- **Trailing**: if checked will eliminate the zeros after a decimal point in a linear alternate dimension.

3.9.4 Placement
- ⊙**After primary value**: is the option by default and displays the alternate units After primary units (see following image)

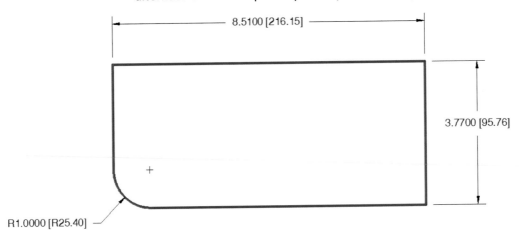

- ⊙**Below primary value**: is the option that shows the Alternate units below the primary units which is a better way than the previous one, especially when dimensions have 3 or more decimal places (see image below).

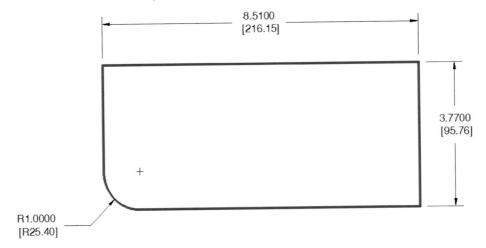

143

3.10   TOLERANCES

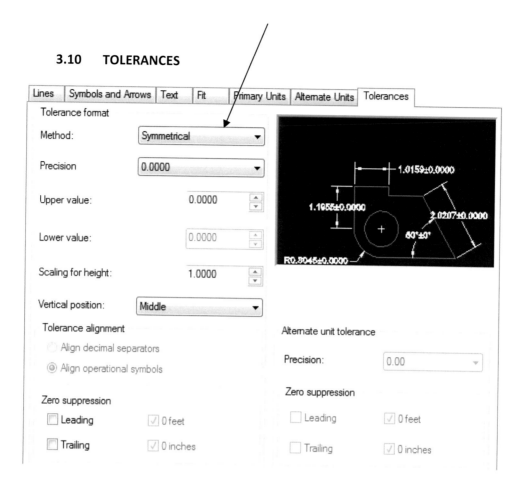

3.10.1 Tolerance format

- **Method**: There are 5 options when dimensioning a drawing in terms of tolerancing:

  1. **None:** which means no tolerances are shown

  2. **Symmetrical:** shows the tolerance symmetrically allocated in positive and negative directions (see image below)

$$\vdash\!\!-\!\!- 3.5\pm0.1 \!\!-\!\!-\!\dashv$$

  3. **Deviation:** shows the upper and lower value of the tolerance

$$\vdash\!- 3.500^{+0.3}_{-0.1} \!-\!\dashv$$

  4. **Limits:** this method shows tolerance incorporated into the basic dimension, which is a practical way of showing the acceptable range of

dimensions. Parts that are bigger than the maximum limit and parts smaller than the minimum limit are considered not acceptable.

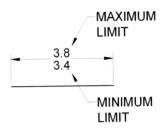

5. **Basic:** this method draws a box around the dimension.

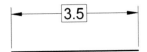

- **Precision:** sets the number of decimal places as required precision for tolerance value.
- **Upper value and lower value:** are used to specify the upper (+), and the lower (-) value of the tolerance.
- **Scaling for height:** is used to determine the height of the tolerance relative to the basic dimension. A scale of 1 will make the tolerance numbers the same height as the height of the basic size numbers. A scale of 0.5 will make tolerance numbers ½ the size of the basic size numbers.
- **Vertical position:** locates the placement of the tolerance relative to the basic dimension (see the options below).

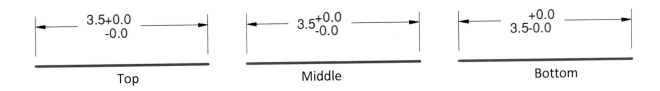

Chapter 14

AUXILARY VIEWS

As described in Third Angle Orthographic section, we can describe the part clearly having one, two, or sometimes up to six orthographic views based on the complicity of the part. When a part has a sloped or inclined surface, then in order to see that surface in a True size we have to see that surface perpendicularly and create additional view called **Auxiliary view** (see images below).

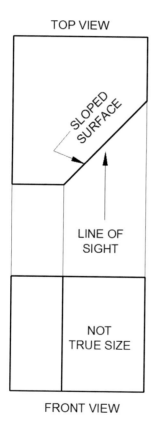

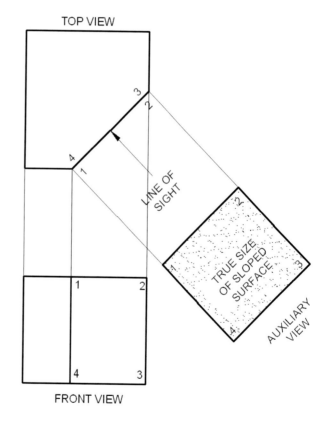

There are two methods of creating an Auxiliary view named:

1. **Folding-Line theory**
2. **Reference-Plane method**

14.1 FOLDING LINE METHOD

Folding-Line theory is used in creating so-called Primary Auxiliary view which could be created using one of the three Principal Projection Planes (Horizontal- **H**, Frontal- **F**, and Profile- **P**). The best way to understand the Folding-Line theory method is to imagine that the sloped surface of the part is a plane or piece of paper glued at the edge around which will be folded (see Simple Folding – Line Theory Method drawing on next page).

14.2 STEPS IN CREATING AUXILARY VIEW USING FOLDING-LINE METHOD AND PROJECTION BOX

This is basically the same method as Simple Folding – Line Theory Method except that the Auxiliary view **will not** be attached to the Top view as shown on the next page. This way of putting the part in an auxiliary projection box is more practical because of the clarity of the auxiliary view especially when the entire part needs to be shown in the auxiliary view – see drawing on next page.

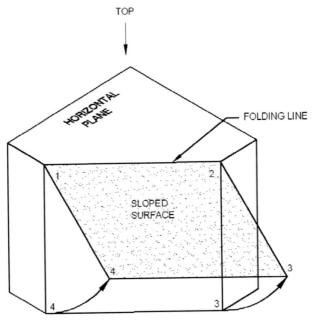

1. Draw a line designated H and F (representing a Horizontal and Frontal plane of the box). This line should be drawn about half a way between the top and front view.
2. Draw lines perpendicular at every point on the sloped line
3. Draw a line designated H and 1 (Horizontal and Primary or first Auxiliary view) parallel (symbol II) to the sloped line and far away from the Top view

4. Number the edges (1, 2, 3, 4) of the slotted surface in both views

5. Draw the Auxiliary view point by point starting with points 1 and 2 by transpiring the distance **H** finishing with points 3 and 4 by transferring the distance **H** from front view to Auxiliary view.

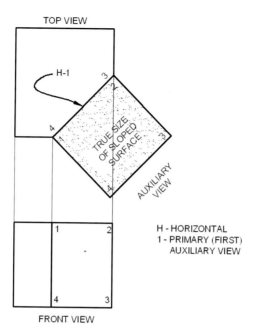

Simple Folding – Line Theory Method

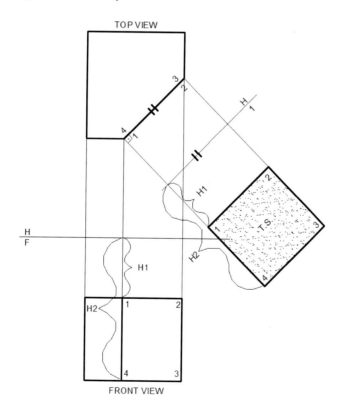

Folding – Line Theory Method using Auxiliary Projection Box

14.3   RULES FOR DRAWING AUXILARY VIEWS USING REFERENCE-PLANE METHOD

Rules for Drawing Auxiliary Views

1. Identify the view in which the surface is shown as a sloped line
2. Place the Reference Plane (RP) line in the other view
3. Draw lines perpendicular at every point on the sloped line
4. Draw RP line in the auxiliary view parallel to the sloped surface and far away to ensure there is room to draw the object.
5. Number the edges
6. Draw the auxiliary view point by point starting from the RP and transport the distance between the points in the true size and shape view.

RULE 1: IDENTIFY THE VIEW IN WHICH THE SURFACE IS SHOWN AS A SLOPED LINE

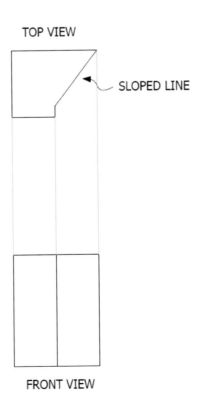

RULE 2: PLACE THE REFERENCE PLANE (RP) LINE IN THE OTHER VIEW

TOP VIEW

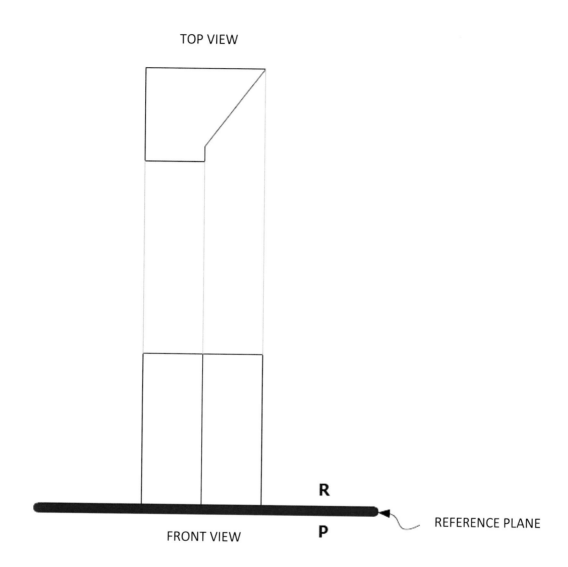

R

REFERENCE PLANE

FRONT VIEW

P

RULE 3: DRAW LINES PERPENDICULAR AT EVERY POINT ON THE SLOPED LINE

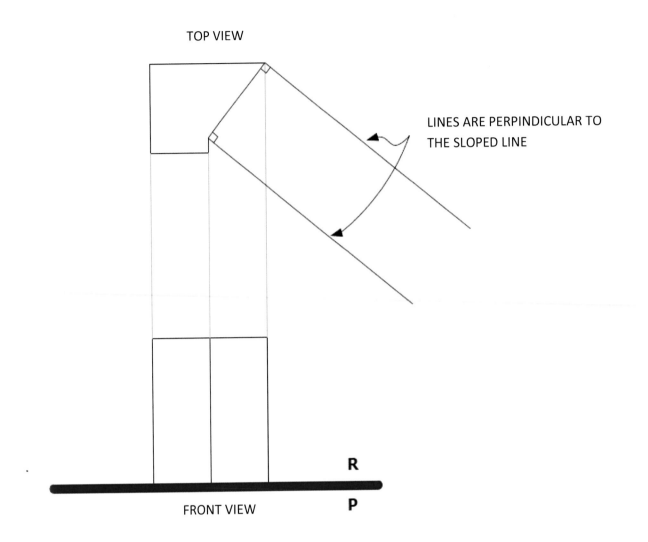

TOP VIEW

LINES ARE PERPINDICULAR TO
THE SLOPED LINE

R

P

FRONT VIEW

RULE 4: DRAW RP LINE IN AUXILIARY VIEW PARALLEL TO THE SLOPED SURFACE AND FAR AWAY TO ENSURE THERE IS ROOM TO DRAW THE OBJECT

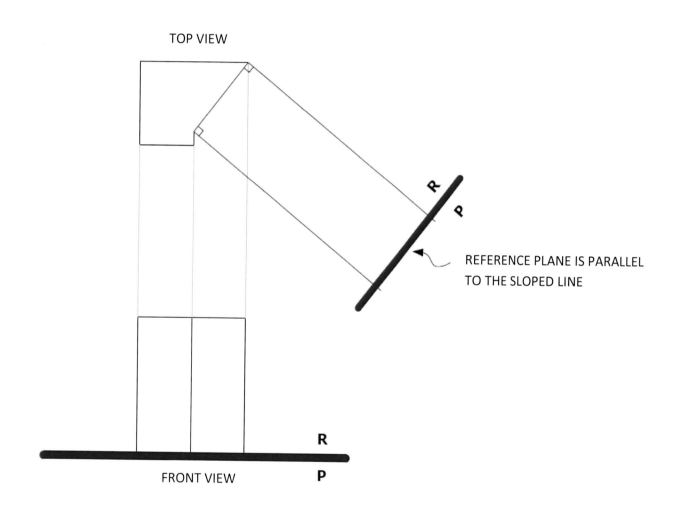

TOP VIEW

R

P

REFERENCE PLANE IS PARALLEL
TO THE SLOPED LINE

R

P

FRONT VIEW

RULE 5: NUMBER THE EDGES

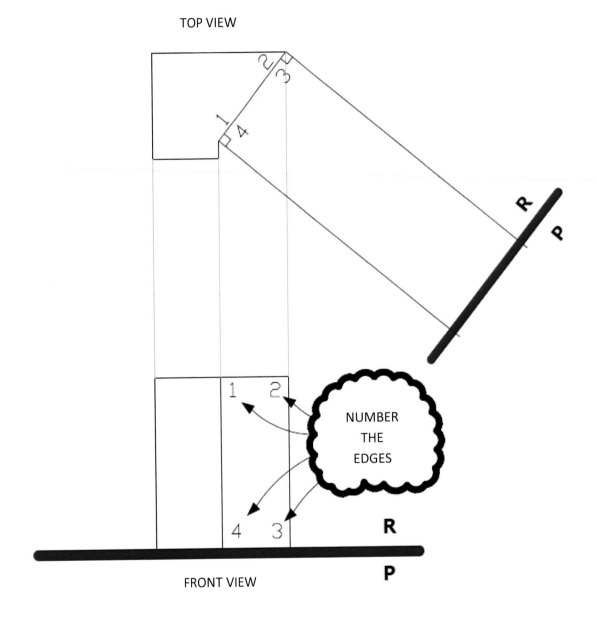

TOP VIEW

FRONT VIEW

NUMBER THE EDGES

153

RULE 6: DRAW THE AUXILIARY VIEW POINT BY POINT STARTING FROM THE RP AND TRANSPORT THE DISTANCE BETWEEN THE POINTS IN THE TRUE SIZE AND SHAPE VIEW.

A: PLACE THE NUMBERS ON THE REFERENCE PLANE

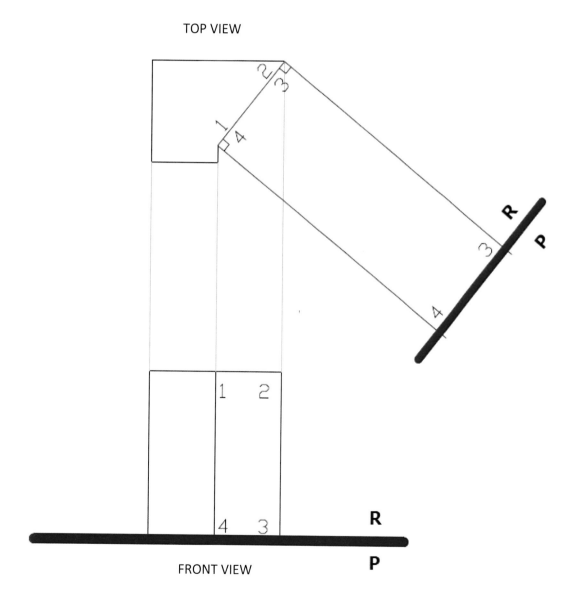

TOP VIEW

FRONT VIEW

RULE 6: DRAW THE AUXILIARY VIEW POINT BY POINT STARTING FROM THE RP AND TRANSPORT THE DISTANCE BETWEEN THE POINTS IN THE TRUE SIZE AND SHAPE VIEW.

    A: PLACE THE NUMBERS ON THE REFERENCE PLANE

    B: USE THE HEIGHT (H) FROM THE FRONT VIEW FOR ONE SIDE

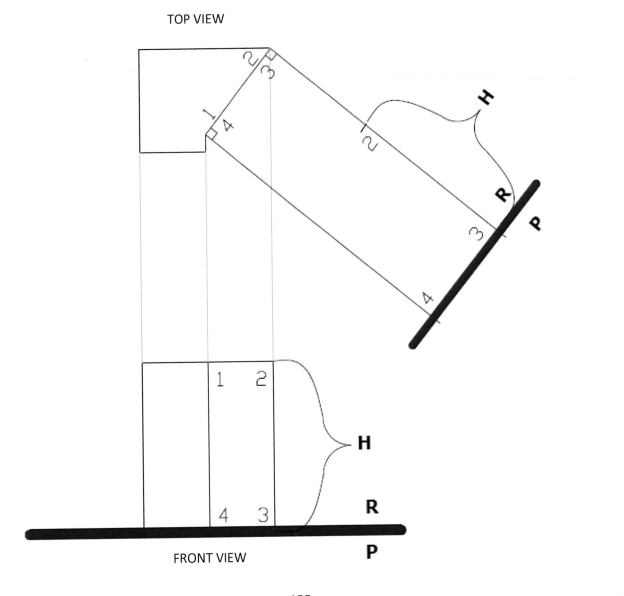

RULE 6: DRAW THE AUXILIARY VIEW POINT BY POINT STARTING FROM THE RP AND TRANSPORT THE DISTANCE BETWEEN THE POINTS IN THE TRUE SIZE AND SHAPE VIEW.

A: PLACE THE NUMBERS ON THE REFERENCE PLANE

B: USE THE HEIGHT (H) FROM THE FRONT VIEW FOR ONE SIDE

C: USE THE HEIGHT FROM THE FRONT VIEW FOR THE OTHER SIDE

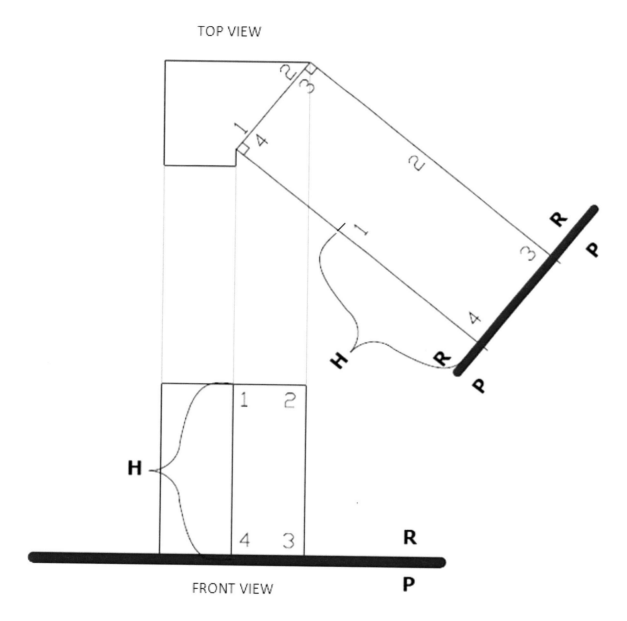

RULE 6: DRAW THE AUXILIARY VIEW POINT BY POINT STARTING FROM THE RP AND TRANSPORT THE DISTANCE BETWEEN THE POINTS IN THE TRUE SIZE AND SHAPE VIEW.

    A: PLACE THE NUMBERS ON THE REFERENCE PLANE

    B: USE THE HEIGHT (H) FROM THE FRONT VIEW FOR ONE SIDE

    C: USE THE HEIGHT FROM THE FRONT VIEW FOR THE OTHER SIDE

    D: CONNECT THE SHORT LINES AND SHADE THE SURFACE WITH TRUE SIZE AND

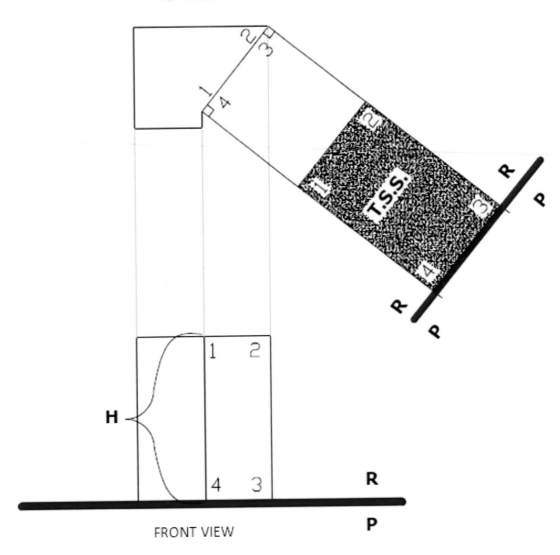

TOP VIEW

FRONT VIEW

Chapter 15

SECTIONAL VIEWS

One of the biggest challenges engineering students are facing is difficulties of visualizing the interior features of a part with all dimensions and hidden lines shown in outside view. For example, the two circles in the part shown below could represent one of the common types of holes such as counter bored or spot facing hole. In order to see the hole and all dimensions and symbols clearly, we need to show the sectional view of the part. Sectional views are created by an imaginary cut through a specific area (line of cutting), removing a portion of it and showing the cut surfaces of the part in a Sectional View. Cross-section lines or cross hatching is used to identify the exposed or cut surfaces. Cutting plane line is used to identify the line of cutting and viewing plane lines are used to identify the direction to view in creating a Sectional View drawing (see all these elements below).

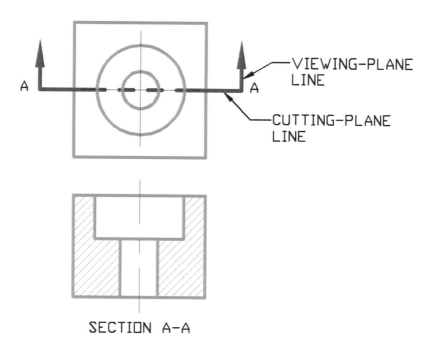

SECTION A-A

15.1 TYPES OF SECTIONS

15.1.1 Full Section

Full section is created when a cutting plane line passes straight though the entire part, removing the front half of the part and showing the cut surface in a sectional view called a **Full Section**. An example of a Full section drawing is shown below.

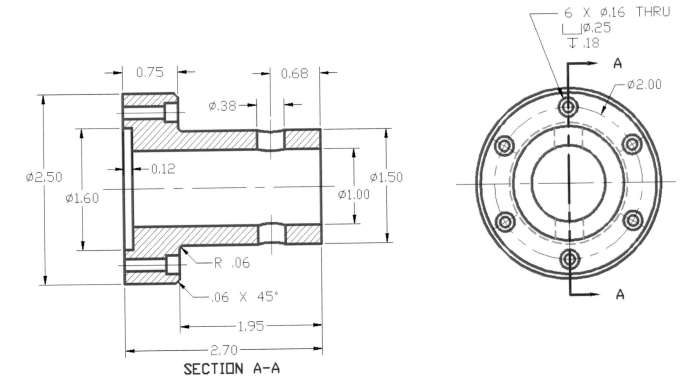

SECTION A-A

15.1.2 Half Section

Half section is normally created on symmetrical parts showing one half of the part in a sectional and the other in standard view. Notice that the cutting plane line in creating half section goes up half of the part and there is only one viewing plane line drawn (see image below).

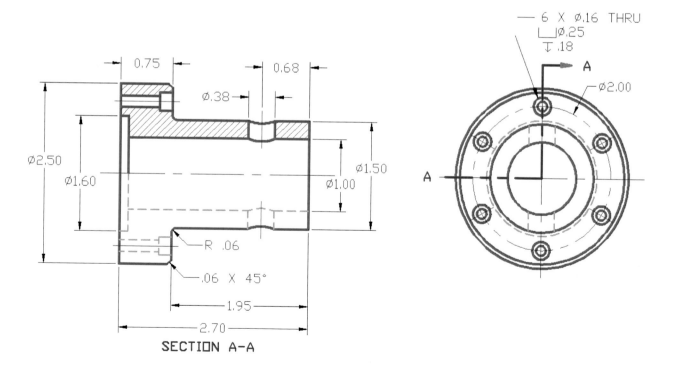

SECTION A-A

15.1.3 Offset Section

Offset section is used when there are some features on the part that are important but cannot be shown using a full or half section because they don't lie in a single plane. For example the part shown below has two small holes, one big hole in the middle of the part and two slots in the lower portion of the part. In order to see all of them in a sectional view, the cutting plane line will go through the small hole first, then offset to the big hole, and offset again to go through the slot (see image below).

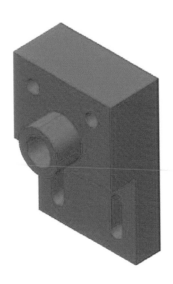

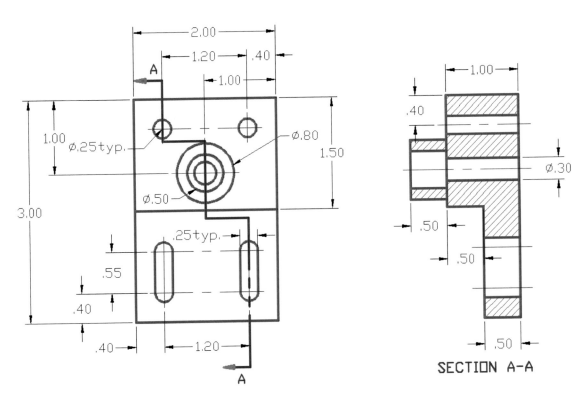

SECTION A-A

15.1.4 Broken-Out Section

Broken-Out section is used when only a small area of a part with important features such as a keyway and a hole for a setscrew are going to be shown in a Sectional View. The purpose of the Broken-out Section is to show only the features that are difficult to see and clearly dimension in a standard view (see drawing below).

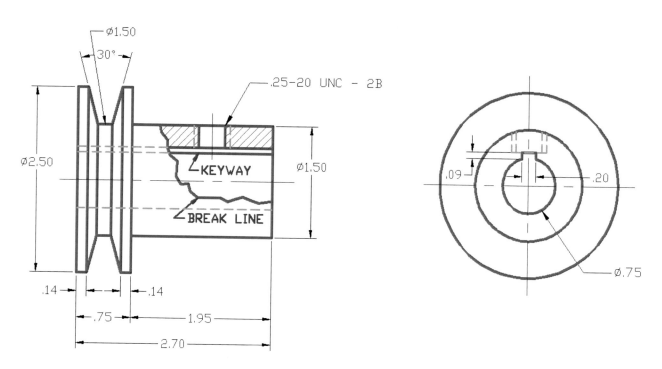

15.1.5 Revolved Section

Revolved Section is a practical way of showing a section of the part in the same view where the imaginary cutting occurred. Revolved Section is created by the imaginary cutting of a small piece of the part, revolving it for 90° and showing it in place as a **Revolved Section** (see drawing below).

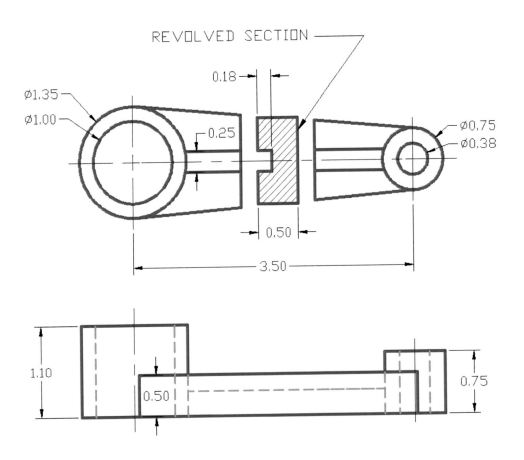

15.1.6 Removed Section

Removed section is a practically revolved section, but it is removed from the view and shown adjacent to it for clarity reason especially when more than one cutting areas exist. The drawing below shows a handle with two removed sections to show the square shape on the left side and a circular shape in the middle of the handle.

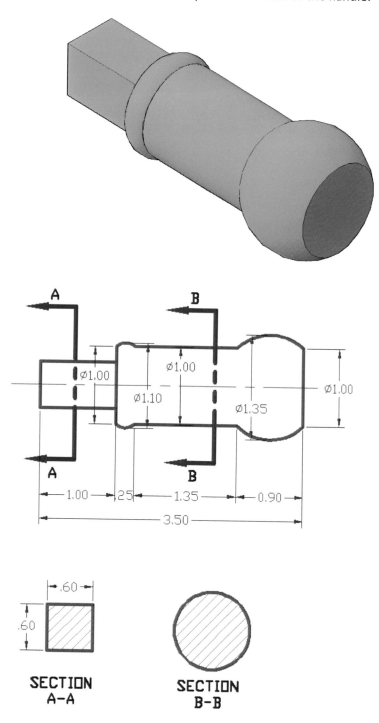

If a part is complicated and several Removed Sections are drawn, then those sections can be drawn adjacent to the view or could be drawn on a separate sheet. If drawn on a separate sheet, then we need to use a special labeling system on the cutting plane line to identify the section and the page (sheet) on which the Removed Sections are shown (see image below).

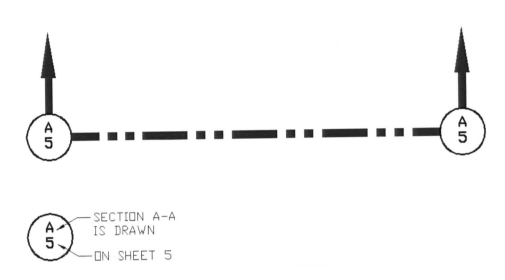

SECTION A-A
IS DRAWN
ON SHEET 5

15.1.7 Aligned Section

Aligned Section is used to show some features of the part that are at an angle when the previously described types of sections cannot be used. For example, on the part shown below there is one small hole in the upper area, a big hole in the middle of the part and a slot which is at an angle to the two holes. In order to see all three features in a sectional view we have to have a cutting plane drawn vertically through the small hole and to the center of the big hole then continue at an angle (in this case 50° to the vertical line) through the slot. In this case the cutting plane line has two parts: **vertical** one, going through the two holes and the second part, **at an angle** of 50° to the vertical one, going through the slot. In order to see all three features clearly shown in one sectional view, we purposely violate the basic orthographic rule to *draw what and how we see*. To create Aligned Section we need to imaginary **ALIGN (rotate)** the second half of the cutting plane line (the one at 50°) with the first (vertical) part before we draw the sectional view (see drawing on next page). Aligned Section when drawn, is practically identical with full section if the slot was in a vertical position aligned with the two holes.

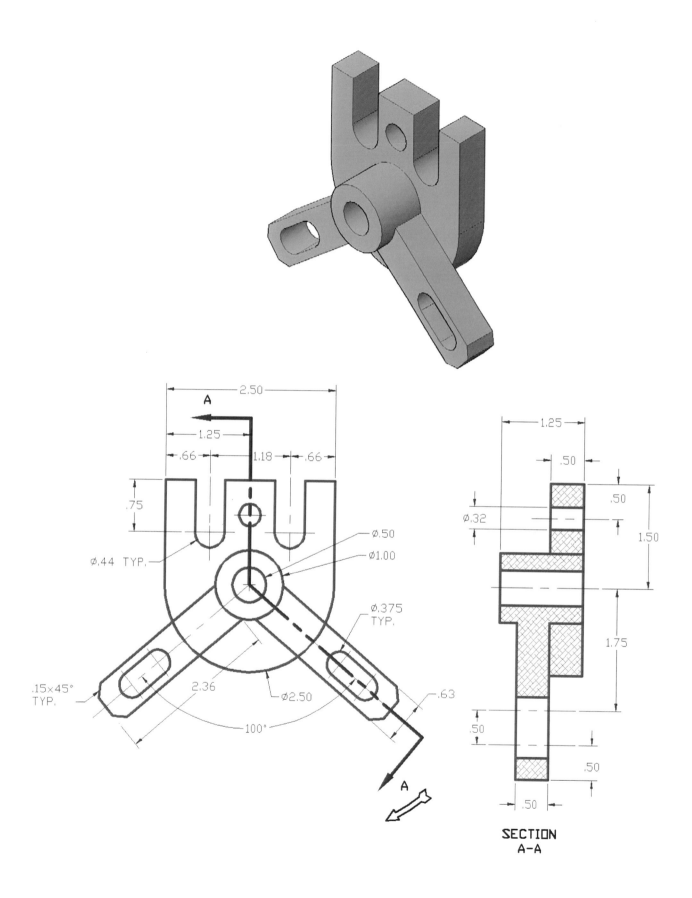

SECTION
A-A

15.1.8 Assembly Section

Assembly line is used to show two or more parts in a Sectional View. When several adjacent parts made of the same material are shown in a Sectional View, then the section lines (cross hatching) have to be drawn at different angles for clarity and easier to identify different parts. If the parts are made of different materials, then we use appropriate cross hatching pattern for that material (see the drawing below and page.... for hatching patterns). When the material is not known or determined a general cross hatching symbol that represents any material should be used. For clarity purposes, standard parts such as fasteners, shafts, rivets etc. should not be cross hatched when shown in sectional views.

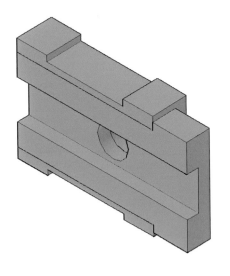

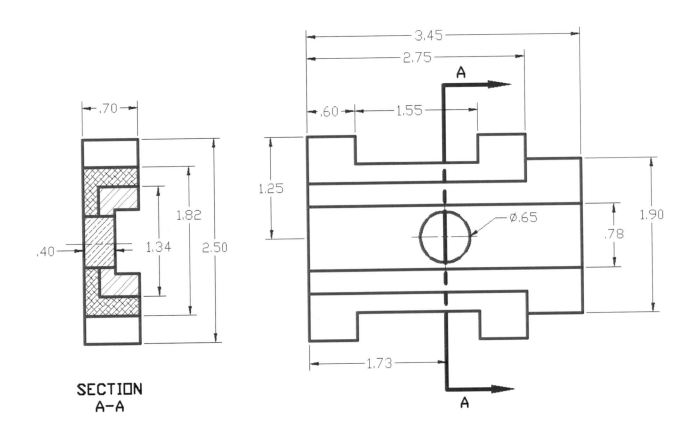

SECTION
A–A

15.1.9 Auxiliary Section

Auxiliary Section is created to see the true size of the sloped area of the part shown in a Sectional View. The basic principle in creating an Auxiliary Section is to draw a cutting plane line perpendicularly to the sloped lines. The **Auxiliary Section** can be a Full Auxiliary Section as shown below, showing not only the section but also entire part, or Partial Auxiliary Section showing only the section.

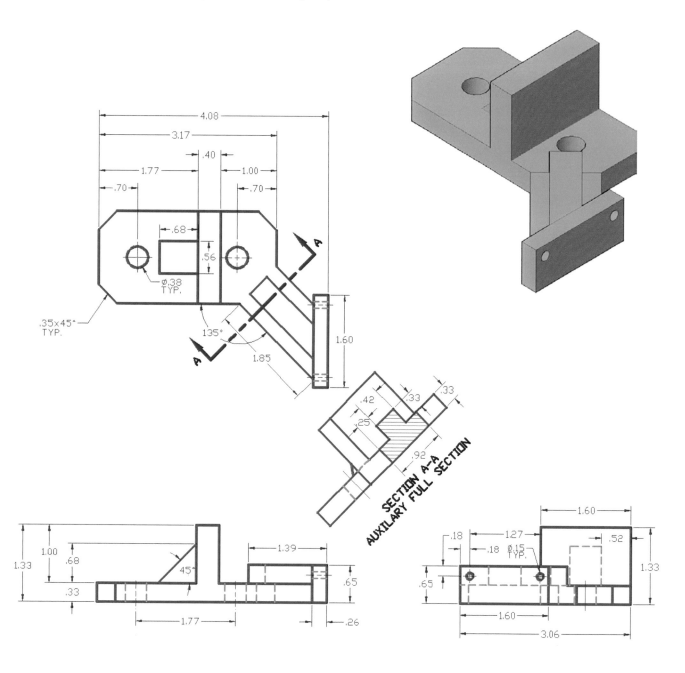

15.2 SOME CONVENTIONS IN DRAWING SECTIONAL VIEWS

1. For clarity purposes, standard parts such as fasteners, shafts, rivets etc. should not be cross hatched when shown in Sectional Views.
2. Thin parts such as plates should not be cross hatched - they should be blacked in.
3. Sectional lines should be drawn at an angle to the outline of the part. They should not be perpendicular or parallel to the object lines representing the contour of the part.
4. Ribs should not to be cross hatched if cut flat.

15.3 TYPES OF HOLES IN SECTIONAL VIEWS

Holes and slots are very common and important features that exist on almost every part. The TYPES OF HOLES AND SLOTS MODEL shown below was created by the author of the book to help students to understand how to draw the holes in top view using ANSI (American National Standards Institute) symbols and more importantly how to draw them in Sectional Views.

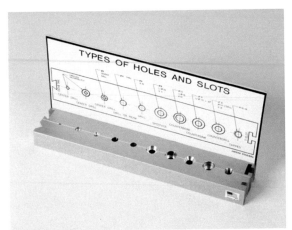

The model shows the views of different holes and ANSI symbols used to identify the parameters of the holes.

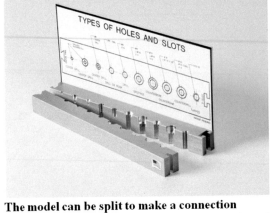

The model can be split to make a connection between the symbols used and the configuration of the specific hole.

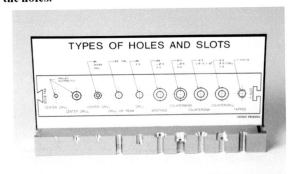

The model can be used to explain the process of making the holes and the tools needed in machining them.

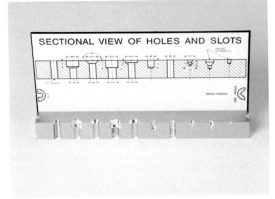

The back of the model illustrates the sectional views of each hole with all dimensions needed for manufacturing.

169

15.3.1 Center Drilled Hole

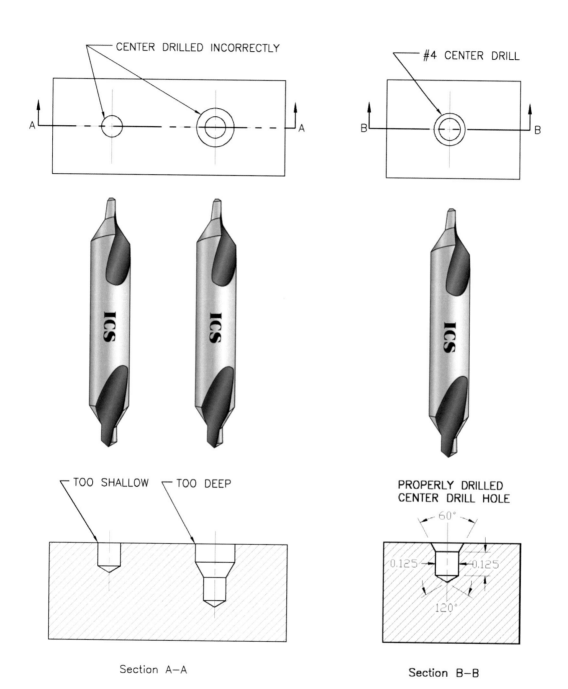

Section A—A

Section B—B

Center Drill Holes are drilled for one of the two following reasons:

1. In order to drill a hole of a bigger size, the first step is to make a center drill hole. The purpose of a center drill hole is to guide the drill to be in the center of the hole we intend to drill.

2. When machining the entire length on long and thin parts on a machine lathe we use a method known as "machining between centers" see figure below. Two centers (one on machine head/driving chuck the other on tailstock) are placed in the previously made center drill holes to support the part while being machined. The importance of a properly drilled center drill hole can be seen from the fact that the angle on the centers is 60° and because of the requirement for a flush contact area and strong support the angle on the center drilled hole has to be the same value of: 60°.

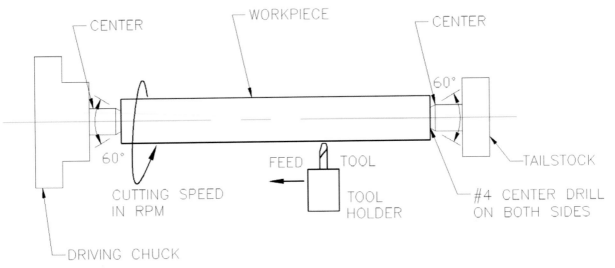

Machining Between Centers

Center drill tools are designated by numbers based on their size (diameter and lengths). There are ten different plain type center drills designated as follows: 00; 0; 1; 2; 3; 4; 5; 6; 7; 8. And their dimensions are given in a table (see drawing below).

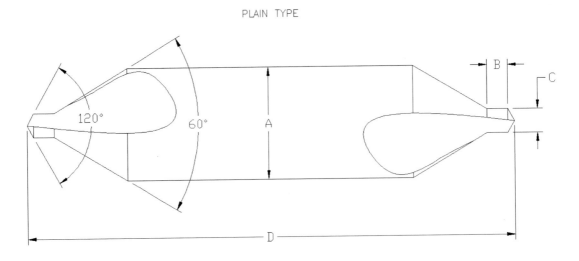

PLAIN TYPE CENTER DRILL				
SIZE DESIGNATION	BODY DIAMETER A	DRILL LENGTH B	DRILL DIAMETER C	OVERALL LENGTH D
#4	5/16 (.312)	1/8 (.125)	1/8 (.125)	2-1/8 (2.125)

It is common practice that saves valuable drafting time to just draw a leader line and the number (Ex. #4) of the center drill to be used, instead of drawing all the elements of a center drill hole.

In some cases to improve the driving force a special workholding device known as a face driver is placed in the chuck to support and drive the workpiece.

15.3.2 Blind Hole

Blind holes are normally drilled for the purpose to be threaded.
Threading/tapping a hole is explained in more details later (see threaded/tapped inch hole). When threading a blind hole it is very important to provide extra depth because the fact that the tap drill tool has 4 to 5 tapered threads. The depth of the threaded blind hole should be dimensioned to the point where full threads end and the tapered threads start.

STANDARD DRILL

Ø.321
↧.500

Ø.321

0.500

Section C-C

15.3.3 Drilled or Reamed Hole

Drilling is one of the most common operations because there is almost no part having no holes. Drills are standard tools and are listed by their sizes (diameter) starting with smallest, ending with the largest standard diameter. There are different drill designs based on their usage. Example:

1. Standard twist drill is the most commonly used drill for drilling standard hole sizes in different materials.
2. Spade drill which is used for drilling from solids (no center drill is used) removing large amount of material.
3. Gundrill, which is normally used for deep drilling hole on guns, requires a special set up and holding method.

Reaming is an operation performed to produce smooth surface finish. Generally reamers could be for manual reaming (having square shank) or machine reaming (with cylindrical or taper shank) by removing very small amounts of material after drilling. The flutes on the reamers could be straight or helical, also the number of flutes is variable (more flutes – more cutting edges and better surface finish). A reamer with maximum helical flutes will produce a very good surface finish.

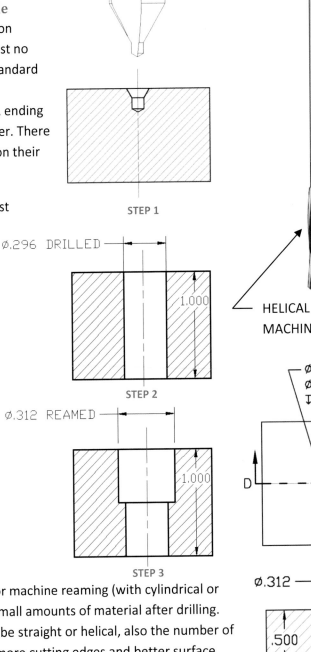

STEP 1

Ø.296 DRILLED

1.000

STEP 2

Ø.312 REAMED

1.000

STEP 3

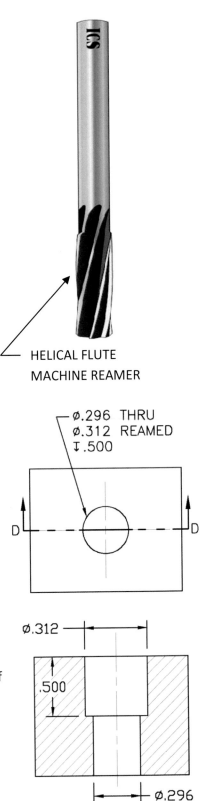

HELICAL FLUTE
MACHINE REAMER

Ø.296 THRU
Ø.312 REAMED
↧.500

D ———— D

Ø.312

.500

Ø.296

SECTION D–D

15.3.4 Spotfaced Hole

Spotfacing as a manufacturing operation that is performed for one of the two following reasons:

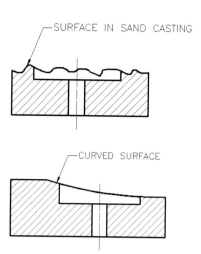

1. The surface on which a bolt head will be placed is rough (ex: surface after sand casting). Using counter boring tool with a pilot (which is preferred in order to have concentric holes) or end mill cutter we remove 2 to 5mm (in depth) of material. To make a flat surface so that the head of a bolt can rest flush.
2. The surface is smooth but not flat.

Notes:

1. Since the depth of a spotface hole is standard (2-5mm) it is common practice not to be dimensioned.
2. The pilot is the part (which could be fixed or interchangeable) of the counterbore tool which goes into the previously drilled hole first and guides the counterbore tool to make concentric holes. It is very important to have the holes concentric in spotface, counterbore, and countersink holes.
3. **This Spotfaced Hole** is made to receive .375-16 UNC bolt with the head diameter of .740

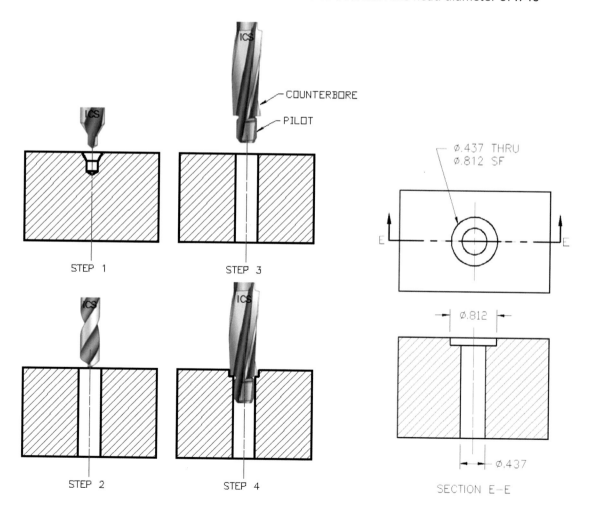

15.3.5 Counterbored Hole

A counterbored hole is a deep hole to receive a socket head cap screw (SHC-screw) whose head will entirely be in the hole, so that other parts can be assembled on top of the surface where the CB hole exists. The size of the counterbored hole is based on the size of the SHC-screw and the type of fit (close or normal) we want to have. The counterbored hole shown below can receive SHC-screw **½ -13 UNC or ½ -20 UNF** with nominal size (major thread diameter) of ½". The process of making a CB hole starts with drilling a small center drill hole (step 1) then drill the hole thru using 17/32" drill (step 2) and lastly (step 3) is drilling a counterbored hole using 13/16" counterbore tool to the depth of .575 to make the hole for the head of the SHC-screw. A counterbored hole could be made using different tools but the counterbore tool with a pilot is the best considering the importance of concentricity of the two holes (Ø.531 and Ø.812) in order to have good alignments of the center of the SHC-screw with the center of both holes.

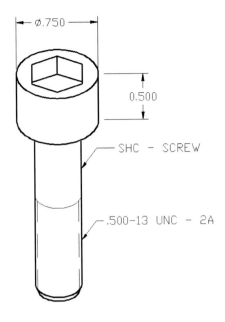

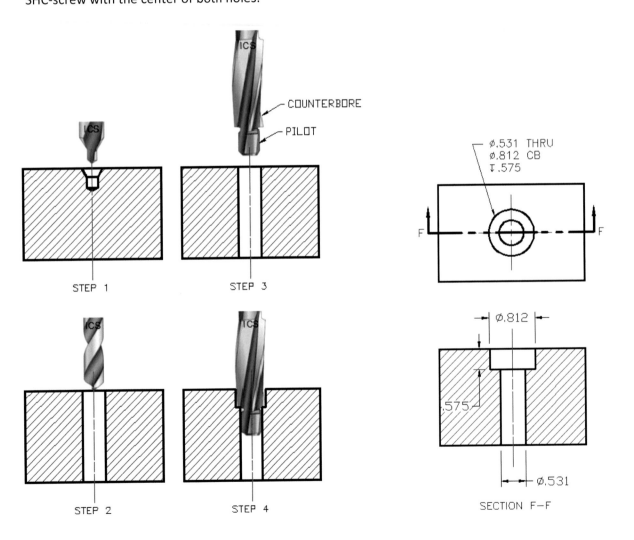

15.3.6 Countersunk Hole – CSK

Countersinking is an operation of making tapered hole or internal chamfer to receive flat head cap screw (in most cases) or rivet.

The angle on a countersunk hole is determined by the type of a thread on the flat head cap screw; for inch threaded screws it is normally 82°and 90°for metric threaded screws. For aircraft fasteners the angle is 100° for safety reason by having larger contact area between the head of the screw and the part being fastened. The steps in making countersunk hole are: 1) make a center drill hole 2) drill the hole for the fastener and 3) make a countersunk hole. There are a variety of countersinks with the point angle of 60°, 72°, 82°, 90° and 100° and different design available based on the purpose of countersunk hole to be used. Generally countersinks could be with odd or even number of flutes. Countersink tools with odd number of flutes reduce chatter (vibration) making better surface finish for the screw head to rest. Also it is important to use countersink with a pilot in order to have concentric holes.

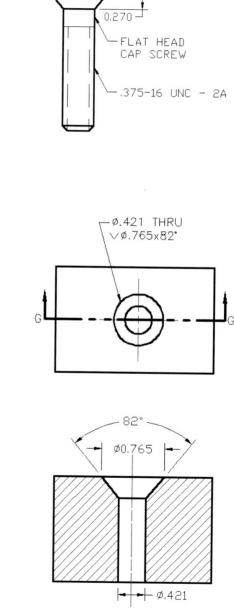

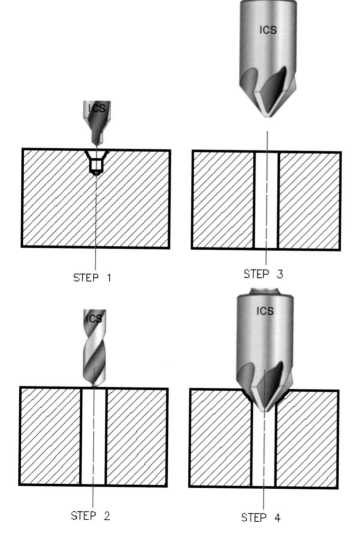

STEP 1

STEP 2

STEP 3

STEP 4

SECTION G–G

176

15.3.7 Counterdrilled (step) Hole –C'drill

Counterdrilling or step drilling is used in two cases: 1) When we want to have a hole with 2 or more different diameters or 2) when we want to have a good surface finish on the hole without using a reamer. In the second case the difference between smaller and larger sizes of the step drills is small so that a small amount of material will be removed with the larger size of the drill and a good surface finish will be produced.

There are 2 options in making counterdrilled/step hole:

Option 1 has 3 steps and uses three different tools:

Step 1 – Center drilling

Step 2 – Drilling the smaller hole

Step 3 – Drilling the bigger hole

Option 2 has 2 steps, uses 2 different tools and is more efficient than option 1:

Step 1 – Center drilling

Step 2 – Step drilling using a step drill with 2 different diameters

Note: sometimes if the size of the small hole is up to 5/16" it is not necessary to use center drill because the smaller size of the drill could be used as a centerdrill.

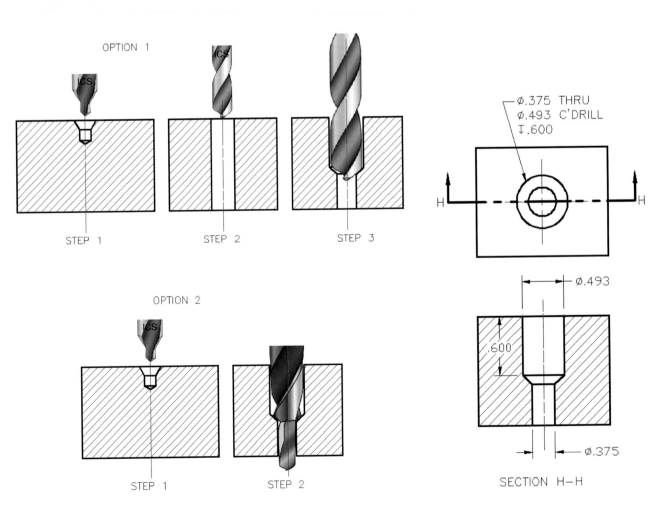

15.3.8 Threaded/Tapped Inch Hole

Threaded holes are commonly used on many parts. It is very important to select appropriate drill size for drilling the hole before threading which is based on the thread designation. The size of the drill should be the same size as the minor diameter of the thread – see below. The value of the minor and pitch diameters are not given in the thread designation, they have to be found from the table for a specific thread. Tapping/Threading operation could be done manually or on a drill press. Tap drill (or simply tap) is the name of the tool used for threading a hole. The shank of the tap drill is square in shape for manual and cylindrical in shape for machine tapping.

Tapping a hole to have a thread .375 – 16 UNC – 2B has three steps:

Step 1 – center drill

Step 2 – drill with Ø.312

Step 3 – tapping

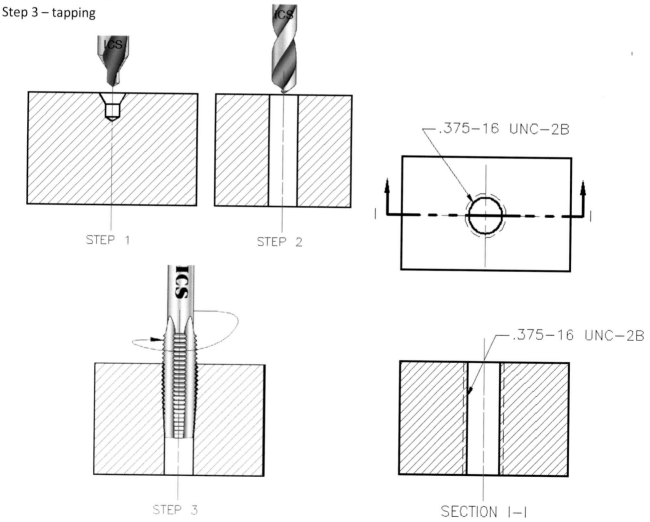

15.3.9 Types of Slots

There are a variety of different slots which are mostly made to allow other parts to slide (move) along them. The most common slots that exist on almost every machine tool are 1) simple slot 2) double angle slot 3) dovetail slot and 4) T-slot. Those slots are normally made on either horizontal or vertical milling machines.

1. **Simple slot** – known as a slotting operation could be done on horizontal milling machine (see first drawing below) using a side milling cutter, or on a vertical milling machine using end mill cutter (see second drawing below)

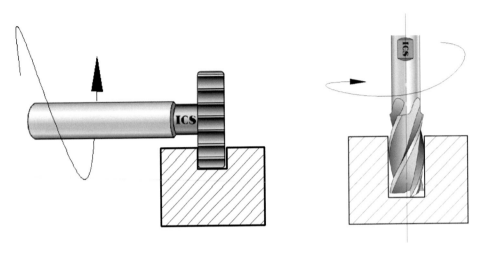

2. **Double angle slot** is normally made on a horizontal milling machine using double angle milling cutter

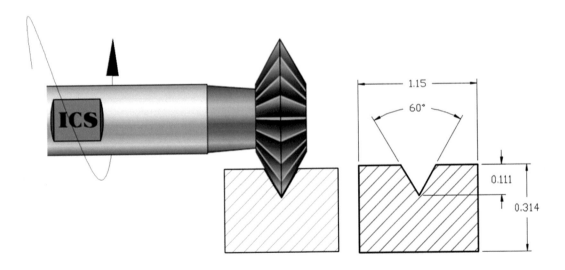

3. **Dovetail slot** is considered a female portion that matches a male dovetail part which can only slide along the lines of the dovetail. Dovetail slots are made in 2 steps:
   Step 1) Making a simple slot (normally bigger than the shaft diameter of the dovetail cutter)
   Step 2) Dovetail slotting

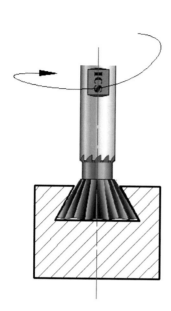

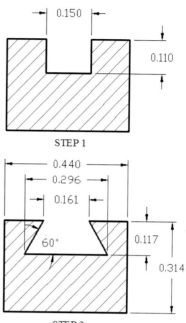

STEP 1

STEP 2

4. **T-Slot** is one of the most commonly used slots on machine tools such as machine lathe, drill press and milling machines. Same as in dovetail case, T-slot is a female part that matches with a male T-slot forming an interlocking joint which enables the male part to slide only along the lines of the T-slot. T-slots are made in 2 steps normally on a vertical milling machine.

   Step 1 – Making a simple slot (normally bigger than the shank diameter of the T-slot cutter)
   Step 2 – T-slotting

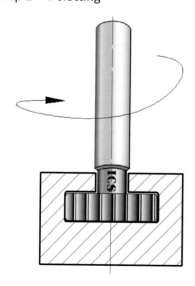

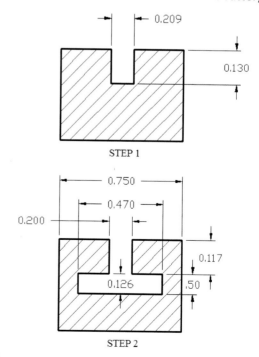

STEP 1

STEP 2

15.4   HATCHING IN AUTOCAD

In a Sectional View, section lines are used to indicate the surface being cut. Sectional lines are normally placed at an angle of 45°, but the angle could be changed to follow the rule that section lines should not be parallel or perpendicular to the principal edges of the part. Putting **sectional lines** or **hatching** in AutoCAD with all options in Hatching dialog box is explained below.

1. Click on the **Hatch** button from the Draw toolbar to have Hatch and Gradient dialog box to be shown (see image below)

Hatch Button

2. **Type and pattern**
    2.1 Type **Predefined** gives us an option to use one of the Predefined ANSI or ISO patterns that exist – Click on ⬚ tab to see the other options (see image below)

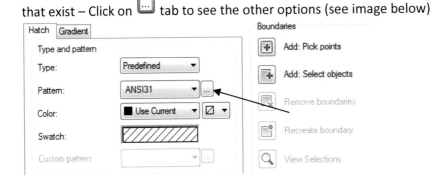

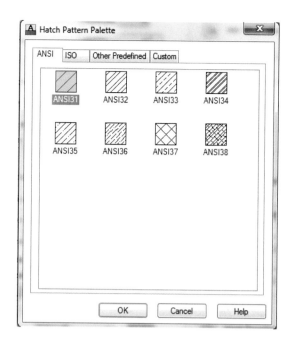
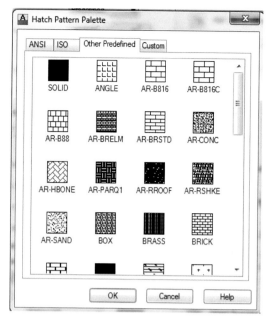

2.2 Type **User Defined** allows us to create our own pattern by specifying the angle and the line spacing. Notice that having angle of **45°** in **User Defined** will create lines at **45°** and having angle of **0°** in **Predefined** will create lines at **45°**.

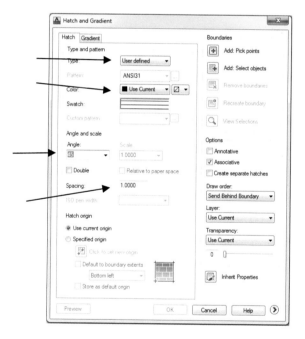

2.3 **Custom** type allows us to use patterns that were custom made.

2.4 **Pattern drop-down list** allows us to select a specific **Hatch pattern** based on the material being used. General Hatching Pattern that could be used for any material is ANS131 and it is shown by **default**.

2.5 **Swatch** shows the pattern currently selected (see image on next page).

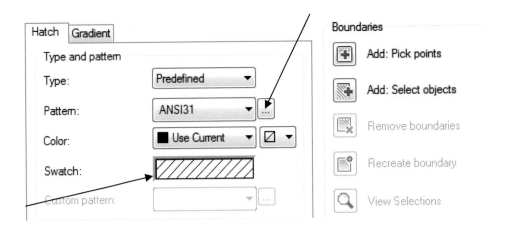

3. **Angle and scale** – Angles from 0° to 345° are available in increments of 15°. Spacing should be based on the drawing size and normally varies from 2mm to 5 mm. A scale of 2 will make the spacing twice the size of standard and scale 0.5 will make it half the size of standard spacing.

4. **Double** will make pattern twice, having lines at selected angle first and second at 90° to the selected angle making crosshatch pattern. Double option is available in User Defined type only.

5. **Relative to paper space** is available in layout.

6. **Spacing** is available in **User Defined** type allowing us to create our pattern, setting up the spacing at a specific value.

7. **ISO pen width** is available in ISO pattern only defining the width of the pen for plotting.

8. **Hatch origin** function is used to set the starting point to be either at the current origin which is at (0,0) point by default or we can set to other position if we want to have better layout of the selected hatching pattern. Example below shows a case of a) having a brick pattern in the area using **current origin** (0,0) and b) hatch origin specified at the starting lower left corner of the area and starting with a full brick (see image below).

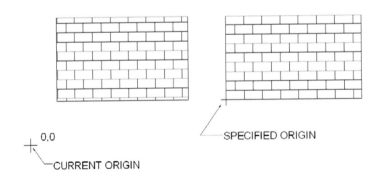

Hatching by using Specified origin: 1) Click on **Specified origin** option; 2) click on **Click to set new origin** button; 3) snap to the lower left corner of the area; 4) click on **Add Pick points**; 5) click anywhere in the area for hatching; 6) right click; 7) select **Preview**; 8) hit **Enter** – see images on next page.

183

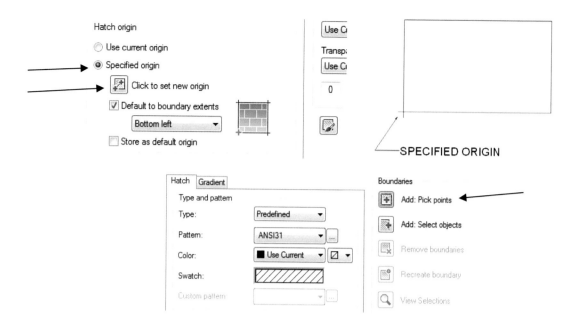

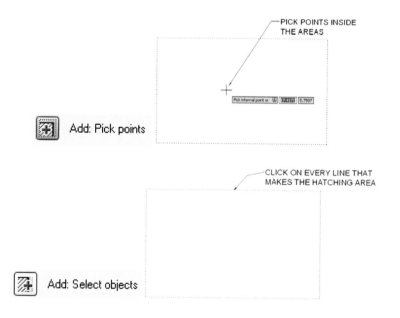

9. **Boundaries** – represent lines that outline the area for hatching. Specifying Hatching area could be done in 2 different ways:

   9.1 Add: **Pick point** – simply pick any point inside the selected area for hatching, you will notice that object lines will change to hidden (see image below)– or

   9.2 Add: **Select objects** – click on all lines that make the hatching area (see image below)

Steps in completing cross Hatching:

1. After hatching area is selected by one of the above described options, **right click** with your mouse
2. Select **Preview** and if you are happy with the pattern in cross hatched area
3. Hit **Enter** to accept

Note: If **Boundary Definition Error dialog box** pops up it means there is a little gap between the lines that determine the hatching area. Solution: Click **OK** and make sure that there is no gap at the intersection of lines that close the area for hatching.

10. **Options**: Keep and use ☑ **Associative** option which is by default.
11. **Inherit Properties** is used to copy existing hatch pattern to another place(s).
12. **Advanced Hatching Options:** If there is more than one object in the hatching area, then selecting which object(s) is going to be hatched may be selected by one of the 3 following options that can be seen by clicking on the arrow to the right of Help button located in the lower right corner on Hatching and Gradient dialog box (see image below).

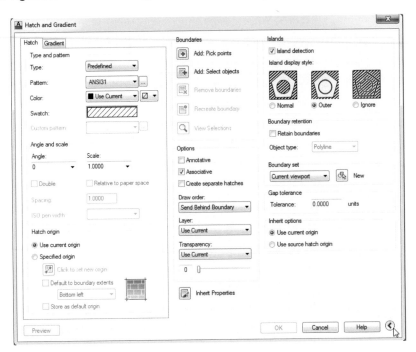

Normal Option is by default, and if selected, will start hatching the selected boundary, skipping the next inside boundary, and will hatch the next one and so on until the last island is detected.

Outer Option, if selected, will hatch the outer boundary only.

Ignore Option, if selected, will hatch all the objects inside the boundary ignoring any islands.

13. **Gradients** are colors. Gradient command, if selected from the Hatch and Gradient dialog box, will display the Gradient tab with **One color** or **Two color** options available (see image on next page).

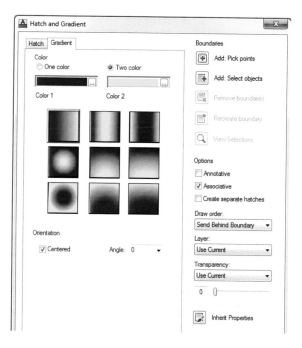

One Color option, if selected, gives just one color with a possibility of making it light or dark by moving the Shade-Tint slider. To select another color click on ⟨...⟩ button (see the image below) select the color, and click **OK**.

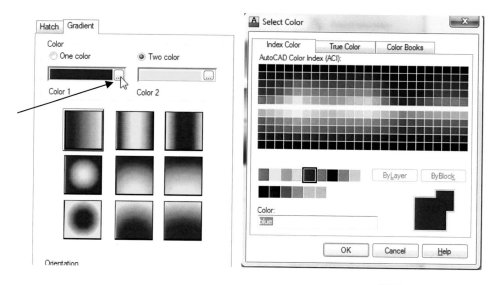

Two Color option shows two colors that could be selected by clicking on ⟨...⟩ button for Color 1 and Color 2 subsequently.

Orientation is by default **Centered** and shows the color(s) in the center of the selected area; the **Angle** rotates the gradient inside the area.

Chapter **16**

MACHINING SYMBOLS

16.1 Machining Symbols

Parts could be produce by removing materials by machining or using other processes that do not require removing material from the part.

If the process requires removing material, then the surface(s) being machined need to have a machining symbol shown in Fig. 16.1.1

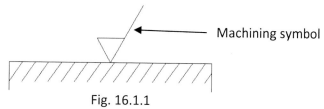

Fig. 16.1.1

If a part can be produced by any other process than machining than we normally use the following symbol shown in Fig. 16.1.2

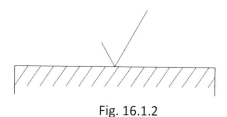

Fig. 16.1.2

When parts are produced by machining we need to provide extra metal which will be removed by machining. That extra metal is called machining allowance and it is shown as a number together with the machining symbol as shown in Fig. 16.1.3

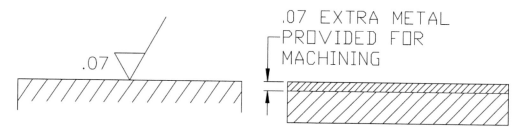

Fig. 16.1.3

If there is a surface that should not be machined than a special symbol called material removal prohibited symbol has to be shown on that surface. See Fig. 16.1.4

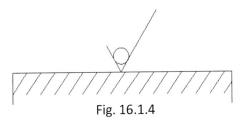

Fig. 16.1.4

If all surfaces of the part have to be machined then we don't draw a machining symbol, we put a note FAO which means Finish All Over. In other words all the surfaces have to be machined. By putting FAO and not drawing a single machining symbol we save valuable detailing time producing a less crowded and easier to read drawing.

16.2 Surface Finish Symbols

Every single detail drawing of a part, besides geometric description, dimensions and tolerances, requirement of the material to be heat treated; requires having symbols for quality of the surface on the part.

A surface finish symbol has certain elements that are shown in Fig. 16.2.1

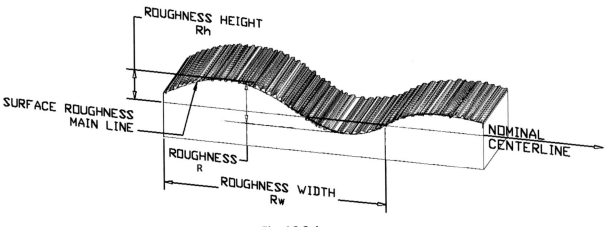

Fig. 16.2.1

All the elements shown on the surface finish symbol have a specific meaning that is very important for proper functioning of the part. It is designers' responsibility based on his/her experience, or on engineering tests, to select proper surface finish symbol in order to achieve the two goals: 1) to reduce the friction 2) to control waste.

Surface finish is very important to proper functioning and the wear of parts such as: gears, piston pins and bearings.

The elements of surface texture shown in Fig. 16.2.2 have specific meaning and importance and they are shown on the surface finish symbol. (See Fig. 16.2.2 below)

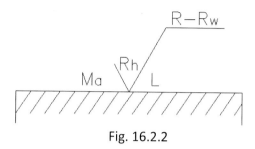

Fig. 16.2.2

Ma – Machining Allowance
Rh – Roughness Height
Rw – Roughness width
R – Roughness
L – Lay symbol

Although each element has its meaning and importance, **roughness height** has dominant importance in obtaining a specific surface finish necessary for proper functioning of a specific part having that roughness height number on its surface.

Surface finish (roughness) is represented by roughness height which is shown as a specific number depending on what measuring system (inch or metric) is used. Roughness height in inch system is expressed in microinches. One microinch is one millionth of an inch (.000001in). An abbreviation for a microinch is **µin**. In the metric system roughness height is expressed in micrometers. One micrometer is one millionth of a meter (0.000001m). An abbreviation for micrometer is **µm**. in the table shown in Fig. 16.2.3 roughness height values are shown in both inch and metric system standard as well as N series of roughness grades.

Roughness Height in µin.	2000	1000	500	250	125	63	32	16	8	4	2	1
Roughness Height in µm	50	25	12.5	6.3	3.2	1.6	0.8	0.4	0.2	0.1	0.05	0.025
N Series of Roughness Grades	N12	N11	N10	N9	N8	N7	N6	N5	N4	N3	N2	N1
Application	Very Rough Surfaces		Rough Surfaces		Smooth Surfaces			Very Smooth Surfaces		Smoothest surfaces used in very accurate measuring instruments		

Fig. 16.2.3 Roughness Height expressed in µin, µm, N series grade numbers and their applications

Lay symbols represent the directions and the shape of roughness marks on the surface. Fig. 16.2.4 shows different lay symbols and their meaning as well as their presentation.

Lay Symbol	Meaning	Presentation
——— ———	Lay Parallel to the line presenting direction of tool marks	
⊥	Lay Perpendicular to the line presenting direction of tool marks	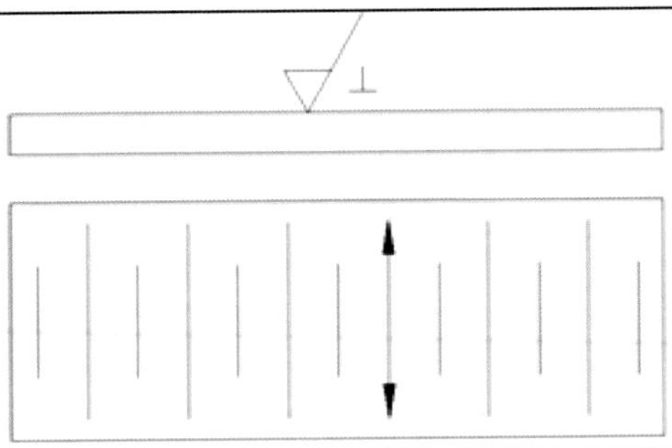
✕	Lay Crossing in both directions on the surface where symbol is shown	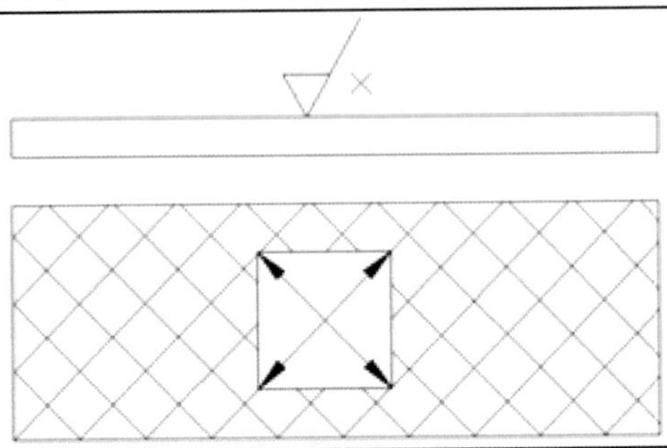
M	Lay multidirectional	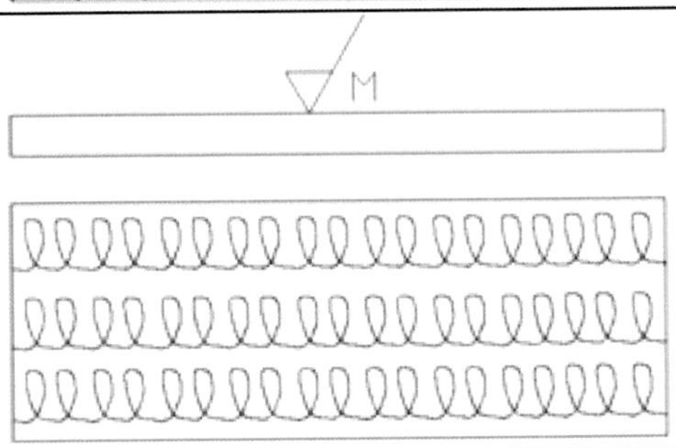

Fig. 16.2.4

There are standard sources in the form of graphs and tables from which a user can find out what production processes should be used to obtain a specific surface finish. For example at the top of the table shown in Fig. 16.2.5 surface finish in µin and µm is shown, and on the left side common production processes are listed.

Process	Surface Finish in µin and µm												
	µm	50	25	12.5	6.3	3.2	1.6	0.8	0.4	0.2	0.1	0.05	0.03
	µin.	2000	1000	500	250	125	63	32	16	8	4	2	1
Drilling													
Milling													
Grinding													

Fig. 16.2.5

In order to select the correct process to obtain 63µin surface finish we need to follow the line starting from 63 going down. If the line crosses between a hatched and grey area (drilling or grinding in the table) we should avoid using these two processes because they might not produce 63 µin surface finish (will be rougher) or the process will be more expensive than necessary. To select the correct process the vertical line from 63 down should cross the shaded area, such as milling in Fig 16.2.5

Once the manufacturing process has been selected (in this case milling) the next step is to determine the cutting parameters: 1) Cutting speed 2) Feed and 3) depth of cut. The cutting parameters in turning are shown in Fig. 16.2.6 below. When milling we should operate with reasonably high cutting speed, fine feed and small depth of cut. Besides milling, 63 µin can be produced by other processes such as: broaching, electro chemical, boring etc.

1) Cutting speed in RPM is how many rotations the machined object will rotate per minute
2) Feed is longitudinal movement (in) or (mm) of the cutting tool per 1 revolution of the part
3) Depth of cut is how deep (in) or (mm) the tool will penetrate the machined object.

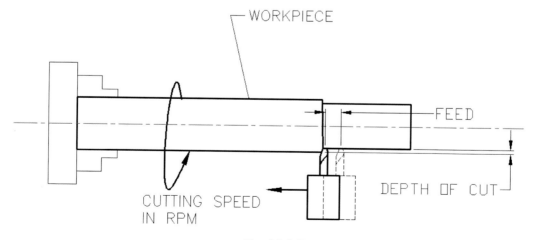

Fig. 16.2.6

Fig. 16.2.7 shown below represents an example of application of surface finish symbols.

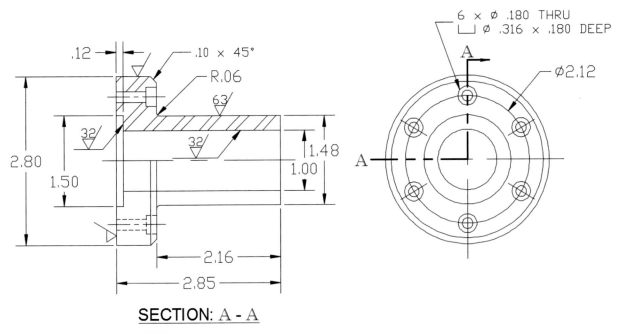

SECTION: A - A

NOTE: ALL SURFACES 125 EXCEPT WHERE OTHERWISE SPECIFIED

Fig. 16.2.7

During the production process and also for quality purpose checking, generally 2 methods for checking surface finish numbers are used.

1) Template, which has machined surfaces as samples to be compared to the surfaces of a part being machined by a machinist. This method requires experience and a very good sense from an operator in order to get relatively accurate numbers. In general this method is not reliable and should not be used when accurate measurements of surface finish is required. A picture of a template is shown in Fig 16.2.8 on next page.

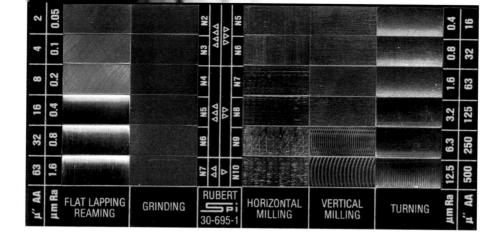

Fig. 16.2.8

2) Using an instrument called profilometer, which could be used for measuring surface finish in both systems, inch and metric by clicking on a single button. Profilometer is amazingly accurate instrument with a tolerance of ±1 μin. Picture of a profilometer is shown on Fig 16.2.9 below.

Fig. 16.2.9

Chapter 17

VIEWPORTS

The space of the AutoCAD program screen can be divided into separate areas that are called **Viewports.** The idea of having the screen divided into viewports is to be able to show different parts of the same drawing. To create viewports do the following steps:

1. Click on the **View** pull-down menu
2. Select **Viewports** and
3. Click on **2 Viewports** option (see image below)

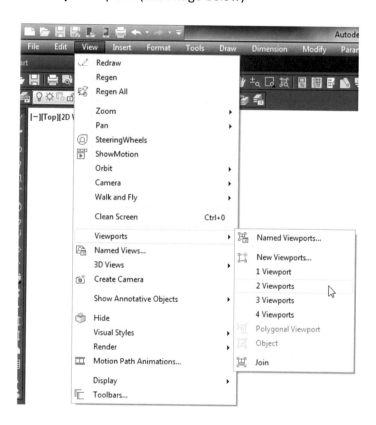

4. Enter a configuration option (Horizontal/Vertical) <Vertical>: hit **Enter** to accept Vertical which is by default – the screen is now divided into 2 Viewports (see image on next page)

Notice that the left Viewport has a thicker border and a graphic cursor which are the indicators that this Viewport is **Active.** Active Viewport means that in order to draw something we have to do that in the active Viewport. In the other Viewport, which is not active, we can see basically the same drawing at the beginning but the cursor is a mouse pointer and in order to make this Viewport to be active we have to click anywhere in that area. Whatever we draw in the active Viewport it will be automatically shown in the other non-active Viewport(s). The idea is by using Zoom and Pan functions to show specific parts of the drawing and see different details in different Viewports. This technique is explained at the end of the book (see Appendix 5).

Before we see how to create 3 Viewports **Click** on the View pull-down menu again, select Viewports, and click on 1 Viewport. To create 3 Viewports do the following steps:

1. Click on the **View** pull-down menu
2. Select **Viewports** and
3. Click on 3 **Viewports** option
4. Enter a configuration option (Horizontal/Vertical/Above/Below/Left/Right) <Right>: hit **Enter** to accept **Right** which is by default – the screen is now divided into 3 Viewports (see image on next page)

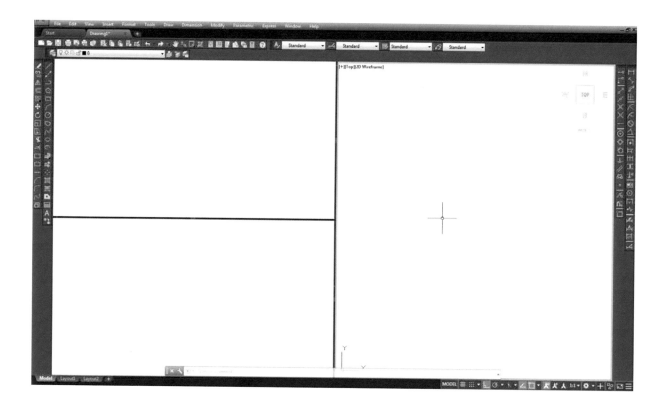

To create 4 Viewports, follow the steps 1 to 4 described above, and in step 3 select **4 Viewports** instead of 3.

Note: Using Viewports in Layout is explained on one of the assignments and it is shown in the Appendixes section at the end of this book – see VIEWPORTS in Layout: Assignment 10.6.

Chapter 18

DESIGN CENTER IN AUTOCAD

Design Center in AutoCAD manages and inserts content such as Blocks, and Hatch patterns. A block is a drawing that represents and object or symbol that could be saved and inserted into another drawing considerably reducing drafting time. Examples of Blocks are shown below.

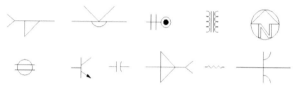

In AutoCAD Design Center there are a variety of different Blocks available to be inserted into a drawing. Below is the explanation of the procedure for using blocks from the Design Center.

17.1   USING BLOCKS FROM THE AUTOCAD DESGN CENTER

1.   The Design Center button is located on the standard toolbar, click on it.

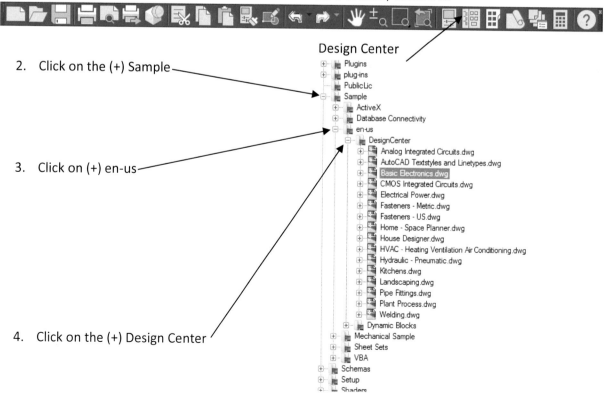

5. Select and click on the (+) of the type of drawing that you intend to create using BLOCKS (Ex: For assignment 11.1 – Electronic Circuit click on **Basic Electronics.dwg**)

6. Click on "Blocks" from the expanded list that opens.

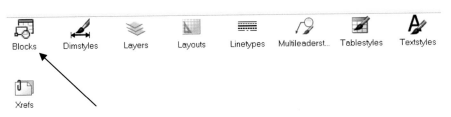

7. In the content area on the right side of the Design Center, you will see Blocks representing different Electronic Elements. **Place your mouse cursor over one of the Blocks, press and hold the left mouse button, and drag the block to your drafting area. Release the left mouse button.** Repeat the process until you have all the Symbols needed to draw Assignment 11.1 or any other drawing.

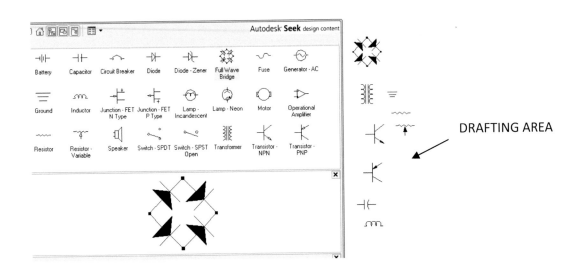

8. Close the Design Center
9. Using your Assignment 11.1 (Electronic Drawing) handout paper, create some lines to connect the electronic symbols as shown in Fig. 23.4. You will need to SCALE, ROTATE, and MOVE the Blocks.

18.1.1 SCALE A BLOCK

1. Command: Type **SCALE** or click on scale button from the Modify Toolbar.
2. Hit: **ENTER**
3. Select objects: Select the Block **TRANSFORMER**
4. Hit: **ENTER**
5. Specify base point: Click the desired base point

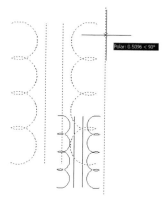

6. Specify the scale factor: Type the Scale factor you need (Ex: "2" will make the block twice as large)
7. Hit: **ENTER**

18.1.2 ROTATE A BLOCK

1. Select: **ROATE** from the Modify toolbar
2. Select objects: Select the **Block**
3. Hit: **ENTER**
4. Specify base point: Select the point that you want to rotate about
5. Specify the Rotation angle: **90°** (or any other angle you need)
6. Hit: **ENTER**

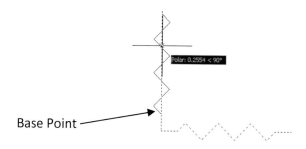

Base Point

17.1.3 MOVE A BLOCK

1. Select: **MOVE** command from the Modify toolbar
2. Select Objects: Select the Block you want to Move
3. Hit: **ENTER**
4. Specify the base point: Select the point on the block that fits the best for the new location
5. Specify the second point: The point where you want the base point on the block to be located

18.1.4 MODIFY A BLOCK

1. Click the explode button (last one the Modify Toolbar)
2. Select the Block
3. Do the necessary changes

18.1.5 COPY A BLOCK

1. Select: **COPY** command from the Modify Toolbar
2. Select Objects: Select the Block you want to Copy
3. Hit: **ENTER**
4. Specify the Base point: Select the point on the existing block that fits the best for the new location.
5. Specify the second point: The point where you want the base point on the new Block to be copied.

18.2 STEPS IN MAKING A BLOCK

1. Draw a Symbol that you want to use to create your drawing (Ex: Desk symbol for the Floor Plan).
2. Use Fig. 1 to locate and click on the *Make Block* button on the *Draw* toolbar. The *Block Definition* dialog box (Fig. 2) will open.

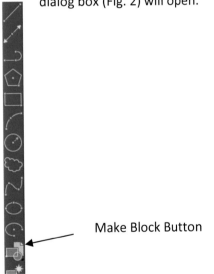

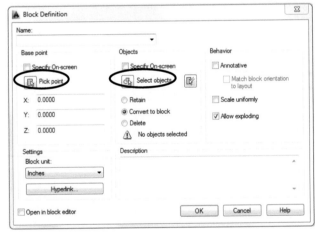

Make Block Button

Fig. 1 - Make Block Button

Fig. 2 - Block Definition dialog box

3. Specify the Name of your block (Ex: Desk)
4. *Base Point* is used to specify the location of the point to be used when inserting the block into a drawing. Click *Pick Point* from the Base point area and then snap to one of the corners on your desk. Once you select a point by clicking on it, you will return to the *Block Definition* dialog box.

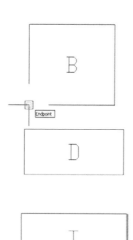

5. *Select Objects*- this area is used to select the objects that will become the Block. Clicking on the *Select objects* will return you to the drawing to select the objects to be included in the Block. Select the object; hitting ENTER will return you to the **Block Definition dialog box.**
6. Click: OK

STEPS IN DRAWING ASSIGNMENT 11.2 – OFFICE LAYOUT

Note: You **MUST** be on layer 0 when Making Blocks
1. Open a new file by clicking on **QNEW** – see image below

2. Click on **Open with no Template – Imperial** button – see image below

3. Click on **Format** and select **Drawing Units** option
4. Select the following:
   TYPE: **Architectural**
   PRECISION: **0'-01/16**
   Units: **Inches**
5. Click on **Format** and select **Drawing Limits** option.
6. Specify lower left corner or <0.000, 0.000>: **Hit Enter** (to accept the lower limit to be at **0, 0**). Specify upper right corner <12.000, 9.000>: type: **200', 200'** (Note: do NOT forget to type the symbol for foot' after 200, to indicate that the limits are going to be in FEET)

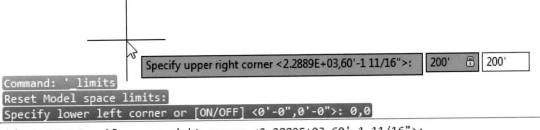

7. Click on: **Zoom All**
8. Following the steps for MAKING A BLOCK, make the Furniture BLOCKS (DESK, TABLE, DRAFTING BOARD, FILE CABINET, DRAFTING STOOL and CHAIR) using dimensions specified in Fig. 1 on the assignment paper. Use text height of 10" for the letters D, T, B, F, S and C.
9. Save them as: **Library 1**
10. Start a new file following the steps from 1 to 6.
11. Draw the walls of the Engineering Department room according the layout and the dimensions shown in Fig. 2 on the assignment paper.
12. Create 8 different Layers, using 8 different colors (6 Layers for the 6 Blocks created in Step 8) and Object Layer for the walls and Dimension Layer for dimensions.
13. Go to the **Design Center**
14. Click on the **Open Drawings** tab.

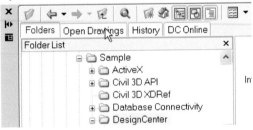

15. Click on the (+) **Library**
   Click on **Blocks** – see images below

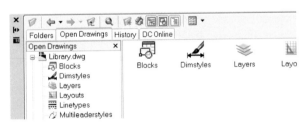

16. Drag The Blocks to your drafting area.
17. Close the Design Center
18. Place the blocks according to Fig. 2 Engineering Department drawing. Note: You will need to Rotate, Move and Align your blocks to get to the required Layout. Also you will need to draw an ellipse for the Board Room table and align the Chairs around it.

Chapter 19

3D SOLID MODELING

This technique is the most effective way of showing the part as a 3D model of a real object with its volumetric shape and allowing us to obtain very important parameters such as volume or moment of inertia. There is no doubt that 3D Solid Modeling is a very efficient tool that helps us to create very complex designs in less time.

In order to do 3D solid modeling in AutoCAD besides the standard toolbars that we use, we need additional 4 toolbars:

1. **Modeling** toolbar
2. **Solid Editing** toolbar
3. **UCS** (Users Coordinate System) toolbar
4. **Orbit** toolbar

To open the above toolbars, **right click** with your mouse over any toolbar currently open. This will open the Toolbar menu from which you select the additional toolbars needed (see the layout below).

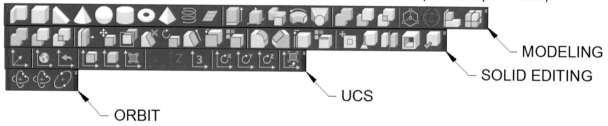

In creating 3D Solid Model basically there are 2 approaches:

1. Using the **3 Easy steps** method which is suitable in creating a complex contour
2. Using **3D Solid Primitives** method mostly used in creating simple 3D solids such as: Box, Cone or Cylinder

Both of these methods will be explained in more detail in the following pages.

19.1   THREE EASY STEPS METHOD

Three Easy Steps Method requires using 3 steps in creating 3D Solid model and it is suitable and faster than the other method of using 3D Solid Primitives especially when creating objects with a complex contour. In using 3 Easy Steps method the first 2 steps are identical (no matter of the shape), but the third one is different based on the shape we want to create. The third step requires using one of the following commands: EXTRUDE, REVOLVE, SWEEP or LOFT. Because the Extrude and Revolve commands are the most commonly used in 3 easy steps method they will be explained next.

19.1.1 Extrude Function in Three Easy Steps Method

Example: _Use 3 Easy Steps method and Extrude command to create the 3D Solid model of the object shown below._

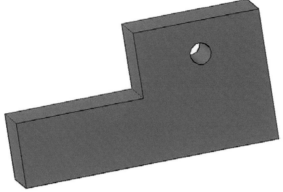

Step 1: Draw a Profile of the Object. In this first step we need to decide which side of the object is best for Extrusion (Extrusion is adding thickness to the Profile of the object). Here is the Profile.

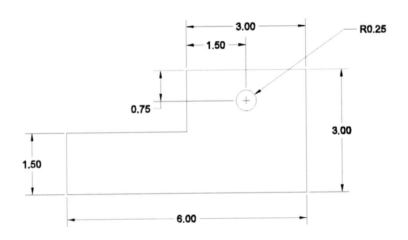

Step: 2 Region the Profile. The **Region** command joints individual 2D entities (lines) and creates 3D zero thickness object out of the enclosed area. The region command is the third last command on the draw toolbar (see image below for Region button location).

REGION

To use the Region command: **1)** Click on Region button **2)** Select objects: window the Profile **3)** click **OK**. Bellow you can see the difference between the Profile before and after using Region command.

BEFORE   AFTER

Step 3: Extrude the Profile. To use Extrude command:

1.   click on **Extrude** button from the Modeling toolbar (see image below)

EX TRUDE

2.   Select objects to extrude: **Click anywhere on the Profile**
3.   Hit **Enter** (you will notice that the cursor is stick to the midpoint of the profile)
4.   Specify height of extrusion: **(type 1.5)**
5.   Hit **Enter**

To see the part in Isometric View do the following steps:

1.   Click on **View from the Pull-down menu**
2.   **Select** 3d views
3.   Click on **SW Isometric** (SW stands for South West) (see image below)

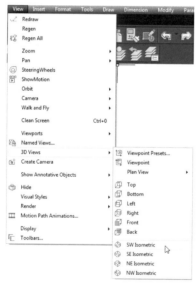

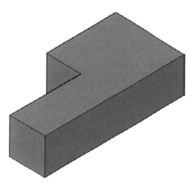

To see the part as 3D Solid object do the following:

1.   Click on **View** from the Pull-down menu
2.   Select **Visual Styles** and
3.   Click on **Conceptual** –the part should look like the following image

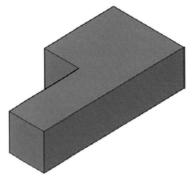

To make a hole on the part do the following:

1. Click on **Free Orbit** button from the Orbit toolbar (see image below)

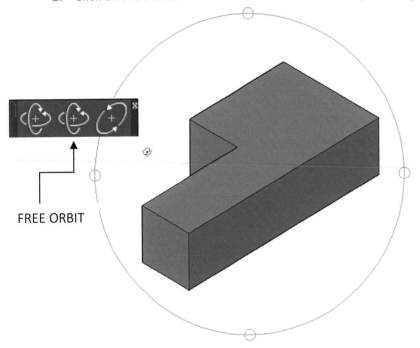

FREE ORBIT

2. Pick a point on the part Click and hold on left button while moving the mouse to rotate the part

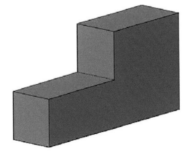

3. Click on **View**
4. Select **Visual Style** and
5. Click on **2D Wireframe** (see image on the next page)

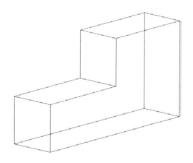

6. Click on **Face UCS** from the UCS Toolbar (see image below)

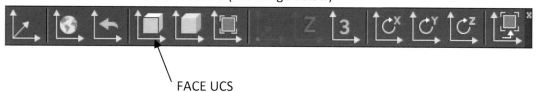

FACE UCS

7. **Click at the lower left corner of the part**. Notice that the coordinate's symbol changed the location to that corner and the front surface has changed to dotted lines which is an indicator that the front surface was recognized as a **Working** or **Construction surface** on which we will be able to work on (see image below).

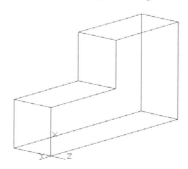

8. Hit **Enter**
9. Click on **Line Command** and create a diagonal line as shown below
10. Click on **Circle command** and create a circle with a radium of R .25 by snapping to the Midpoint of the diagonal line to be symmetrically located as shown below

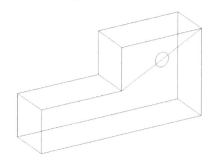

11. Click on **Region** button

12. Click on the **Circle**

13. Hit **Enter**

14. Click on **Extrusion button** from the Modeling toolbar

15. Click on the **Circle** to select objects and then

16. Hit **Enter**

17. Move the Cursor to **create a Cylinder** like one shown below

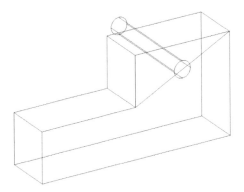

18. Now we do have 2 objects that are 3D Solids: one is the **Block** and the other is the **Cylinder**. In order to have one single object **A BLOCK WITH A HOLE** we need to Subtract the Cylinder from the Block by using so called **Boolean Subtract operation**. Note: Boolean Operation will be explained in more details later. Below you will find how to use Subtract Boolean operation to make the hole and complete the part.

19. Click on **Subtract** button from the Modeling Toolbar (see image below for the location of Subtract button)

SUBTRACT

20. Select objects: **Click anywhere on the Block**

21. Hit **Enter**

22. Select objects: **Click on the Cylinder**

23. Hit **Enter**. Notice that the cylinder was shortened and became a Hole on the Block (see part on next page).

24. **Erase** the diagonal line

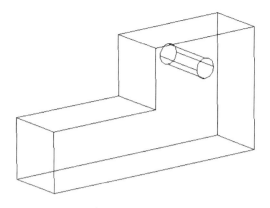

25. Click on **View** from the Pull-down menu
26. Select **Visual Styles** and
27. Click on **Conceptual** –the rendered part should like one shown below

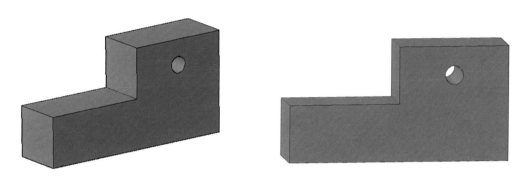

28. Use Free Orbit Command and rotate the part to see the hole

19.1.1 Revolve Function in Three Easy Steps Method

If the shape is cylindrical having different diameters, some round, chamfers and other features, than instead of using Extrusion it is better to use **Revolve function** which is explain on an example below.

Example: *Use 3 Easy Steps method and Revolve command to create the 3D Solid model of the object shown on next page.*

Step 1: Draw a Profile of the Object.

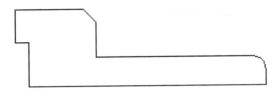

Step: 2 Region the Profile.

Step 3: Revolve the Profile. In order to Revolve the profile we need to have an axis which is shown below with the profile.

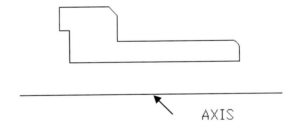

AXIS

To use Revolve command:

1.   Click on **Revolve** button from the Modeling toolbar (see image below)

REVOLVE

2.   Select objects to revolve: **click anywhere on the profile**

3.   Hit **Enter**
4.   Specify axis start point or define axis by ( ) <object>: snap to one end of the line then snap to the other end of the line (axis) below the profile
5.   Specify angle of revolution or (start angle) <360>: **Hit Enter** to accept the angle of rotation to be 360° (see the image of the part below)

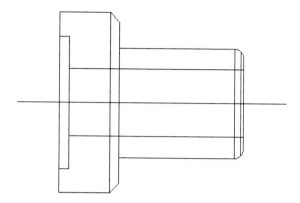

6.   To see the part in an Isometric View do the following:

     6a.   click on **View** from the Pull-down menu

     6b.   select **3D Views** and

     6c.   Click on **SW** (South West) view (see the view below)

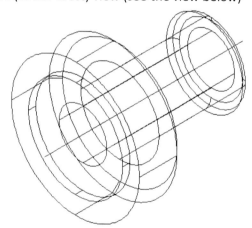

To see the part as 3D Solid object do the following:

1.   Click on **View** from the Pull-down menu
2.   Select **Visual Styles** and
3.   Click on **Conceptual** –the part should like one shown on next page
4.   Erase the axis

19.2 3D SOLID MODELING USING 3D SOLID PRIMITIVES

This method is based on using common **Geometric Primitives** that are available in AutoCAD and are located in Modeling Toolbar (see below).

STEPS IN CREATING PRIMITIVES
In order to see the entire process of creating the Primitives in Isometric view:

1. Click on **View** from the Pull-down menu
2. Select **3D Views**
3. Click on **SW**

19.2.1 To create a BOX:

1. Click on the **Box button** from the Modeling toolbar (see image below)

BOX

2. Specify the first corner or (Center): **Click at any point**
3. Specify other corner or (Cube/Length): **click at any point** to specify **the other corner**
4. Specify height or (2 Points): **click at any point** to specify the height (see image on next page)

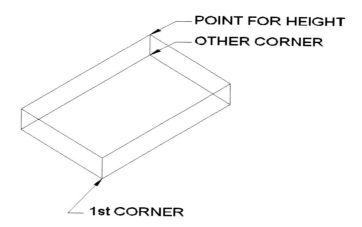

POINT FOR HEIGHT
OTHER CORNER
1st CORNER

5. Note: A **Box** could be created if we know the **Length**, **Width** and **Height** and we specify their values in step 3. Here is the procedure:
6. Click on the Box button from the Modeling toolbar
7. Specify the first corner or (Center): **Click at any point**
8. Specify other corner or (Cube/Length): type it **L** (for length)
9. Hit **Enter**
10. Specify length: type it **5** and hit **Enter**
11. Specify width: **4** and hit **Enter**
12. Specify height: **2** and hit **Enter**

19.2.2 To create a WEDGE:

1. Click on the **Wedge button** from the Modeling toolbar
2. Specify the first corner or (Center): **click at any point**
3. Specify other corner or (Cube/Length): **click at any point** to specify **the other corner**
4. Specify height or (2 points): **click at any point** to specify the height (see image below)

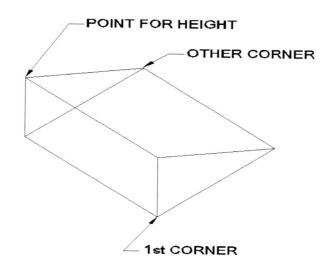

POINT FOR HEIGHT
OTHER CORNER
1st CORNER

213

19.2.3 To create a CONE:

1. Click on the **Cone button** from the Modeling toolbar
2. Specify center point of base or (....): **click on any point** for center or if you want a specific point **Click** on it
3. Specify base radius (or Diameter): **click on any point** or type the value for Radius
4. Specify height or (.....): **click on any point** or type the value for the height (see image below)

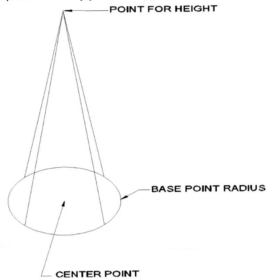

19.2.4 To create a SPHERE:

1. Click on the **Sphere button** from the Modeling toolbar
2. Specify center point or (....): **click on any point** for center
3. Specify radius or(Diameter) < >: **click on any point** or type the value for **Radius** and hit **Enter** (see image below)

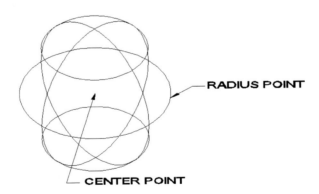

19.2.5 To create a CYLINDER:

1. Click on the **Cylinder** button from the Modeling toolbar
2. Specify center point of base or (...): click on any point for center

3. Specify base radius or(Diameter) < >: click on any point or type the value for **Radius** and hit **Enter**
4. Specify height or (.....): click on any point or type the value for the **Height** (see image below)

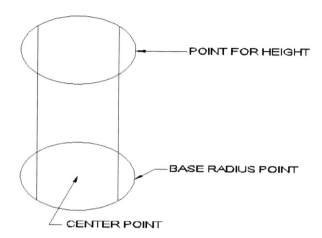

POINT FOR HEIGHT

BASE RADIUS POINT

CENTER POINT

19.2.6 To create a TORUS:

1. Click on the **Torus button** from the Modeling toolbar
2. Specify center point or (....): **click on any point** for center
3. Specify radius or(Diameter) < >: **click on any point** or type the value for **Torus Radius** and hit **Enter**
4. Specify tube radius or (2Point/Diameter): **click on any point** or type the value for **Tube Radius** and hit **Enter** (see image below)

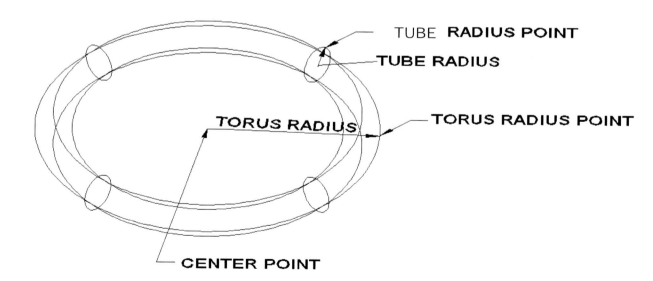

TUBE **RADIUS POINT**

TUBE RADIUS

TORUS RADIUS POINT

TORUS RADIUS

CENTER POINT

19.2.7 To Create a PYRAMID:

1. Click on the **Pyramid button** from the Modeling toolbar
2. Specify center point of base or (Edge/Sides): **click on any point** for center
3. Specify base radius or(Inscribed) < >: **click on any point** or type the value for **Radius** and hit **Enter**
4. Specify height or (......) <..>: **click on any point** or type the value for the **Height** (see image below)

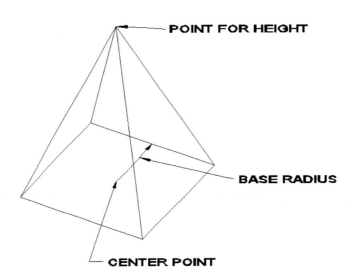

19.3 BOOLEAN OPERATIONS WITH SOLIDS

Knowing now how to create different basic shapes using Primitives from the Modeling toolbar we can combine those basic shapes into more complicate shapes using so called **BOOLEAN Operation** that will be explained on the next page.

There are 3 Boolean Operations:

1. **UNION** designated by a standard symbol (∪)
2. **SUBTRACT** with a standard symbol (−)
3. **INTERSECT** with a standard symbol (∩)

To see how these operations work, create a **Box** and a **Cone** as shown on next page. Use Face UCS to select the top surface of the **Box** for the base of the **Cone**. These two objects are separate solids that will be used in the explanation below to see how the 3 Boolean operations work.

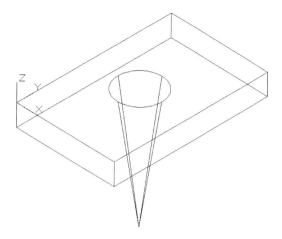

19.3.1 UNION

Union operation creates a 3D solid by **joining** any number of 3D solids (in our case 2 solids - a **Box** and a **Cone**). To use Union operation:

1. Click on **Union** button from the Modeling toolbar (see image below)

UNION

2. Select objects: **click on the Box and the Cone** (or window both of them)

3. Hit **Enter** – the image we just created is now a single 3D Solid object (see image below)

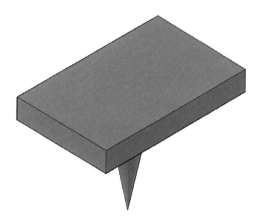

19.3.2 SUBTRACT

Subtract operation creates a 3D solid by subtracting one 3D solid from another 3D solid. To use Subtract operation:

1. Click on Subtract button from the Modeling toolbar (see image below)

SUBTRACT

2. Select objects (to Subtract FROM): **Click on the Box**
3. Hit **Enter**
4. Select objects (to Subtract): **Click on the Cone**
5. Hit **Enter (**see the images below). We have just created a box with a tapered hole on it.

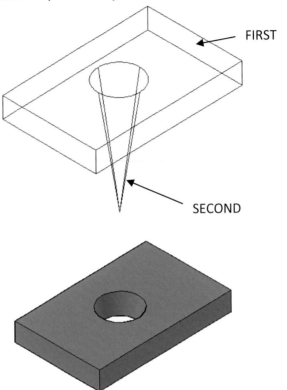

FIRST

SECOND

Note: It is extremely important to follow the sequence of selecting the objects: CLCIK ON OBJECT TO SUBTRACT FROM (a Box in this case) <u>first</u>, and then CLICK ON THE OBJECT TO SUBTRACT <u>second </u>(a Cone in this case). If we change the sequence and click on the Cone first and on the Box second, the 3D solid that will be created (in this case shortened Cone) will be totally different than the one created above (a Box with a tapered hole) – see the image of the shortened cone on next page.

19.3.3 INTERSECT

Intersect operation creates a 3D solid that consists of the common area between the solids participating in this operation. To use Intersect operation:

1. Click on Intersect button from the Modeling toolbar (see image below)

INTERSECT

2. Select objects : **Click on the Box** then
3. **Click on the Cone**
4. Hit **Enter.** We have just created a 3D solid (a short Cone) as a common area between the Box and the Cone (see image below).

Chapter 20

THREAD DESIGNATION

From the variety of standard thread forms that exist, the following two forms are most commonly used:

1. UNIFIED NATIONAL (UN or Inch) standard thread form and
2. ISO – International (Metric) standard thread form

20.1 UNIFIED NATIONAL (Inch) EXTERNAL THREAD DESIGNATION

A simplified representation of Inch External Thread with all the elements of the designation is shown in Fig. 1 below.

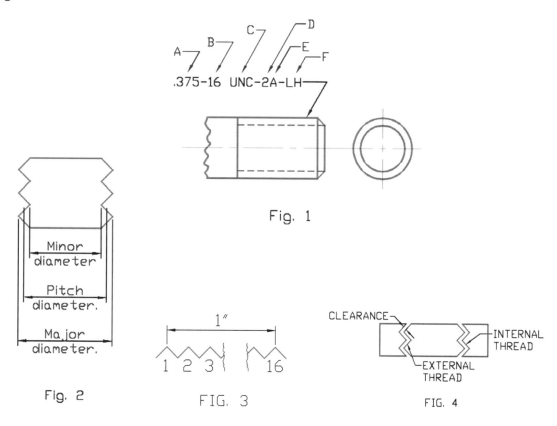

Fig. 1

Fig. 2

FIG. 3

FIG. 4

A- **.375 – Major diameter** (see Fig. 2)
B- **16 – Pitch (number of threads per 1")** (see Fig. 3)
C- **UNC – Thread Series**
There are 5 standard thread series:

UNC – **U**nified **N**ational **C**oarse

UNF – **U**nified **N**ational **F**ine

UNEF – **U**nified **N**ational **E**xtra **F**ine

UNM – **U**nified **N**ational **M**iniature

UN – **U**niform **P**itch

D- **Thread Class.** According to ANSI (American National Standards Institute) there are 3 Classes (class 1, 2, and 3) of threads based on the amount of clearance (allowance between external and internal threads (see Fig. 4). Class 1 Thread has the biggest clearance and is used on coarse thread for quick assembly.

E- **A** – is used to identify **External thread** and letter **B** – for **Internal thread**

F- **LH** – Left Handed thread (Normally threads are Right Handed in which case no designation is required for a Right Handed thread)

DRAWING INTERNAL INCH THREAD

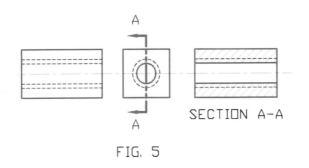

FIG. 5

20.2 ISO- (METRIC) EXTERNAL THREAD DESIGNATION

A simplified representation of Metric external thread with all the elements of its designation is shown in Fig. 6 below.

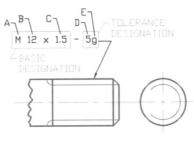

FIG. 6

A- **M** – stands for **Metric**

B- **12** – **Major Diameter** in (mm) – see Fig. 7

C- **1.5** – **Pitch** (distance between two corresponding Crests expressed in mm) – see Fig. 7

D- **Tolerance grade** There are 7 tolerance grades designated as: 3, 4, 5, 6, 7, 8, 9 (Numbers 3, 4, and 5 represented fine thread, number 6 is a medium quality thread and numbers 7, 8, and 9 represent coarse thread

E- **Tolerance position** basically determines the clearance/allowance between external and internal thread. Tolerance positions for external threads are: **e** – large allowance, **g** – small allowance

221

and **h** – very small allowance. For internal threads: **G** – small allowance and **H** – very small allowance

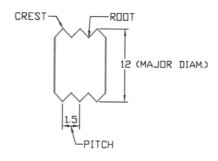

FIG. 7

DRAWING INTERNAL METRIC THREAD

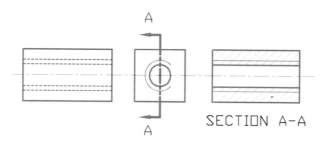

FIG. 8

Chapter 21

Welding Symbols

21.1 Standard Welding Symbol with its Parameters

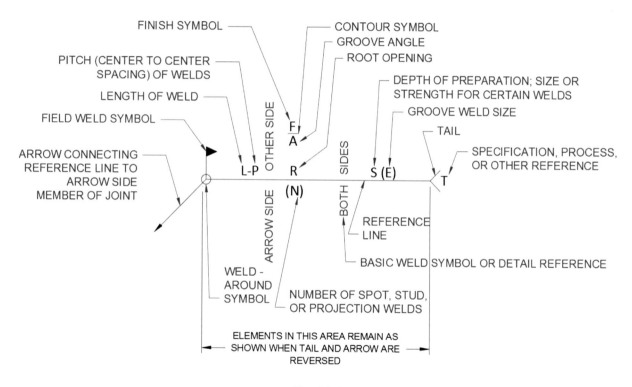

Fig. 21.1

The welding symbol with the parameters shown on it (see figure 21.1 above) is a guide and at the same time a requirement for a welder to complete the welding job. Welding symbols are in accordance with the American welding society document AWS A2.4-1986.

For practical reasons and so a student can better understand the meaning of each element of a welding symbol the following welding symbol Fig. 21.2 is shown below with an explanation of each element and its variations.

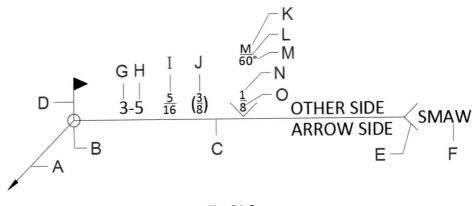

Fig. 21.2

A – Leader line connecting the reference line C and a joint.

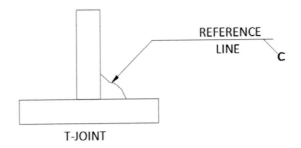

T-JOINT

B – Weld-all-around symbol is used when we need to form a continuous weld that finishes at the starting point. It is not necessary for the shape of the part to always be round in order to include the all around weld. Some examples of different shapes are shown below.

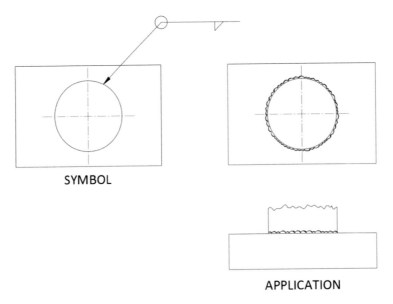

SYMBOL

APPLICATION

224

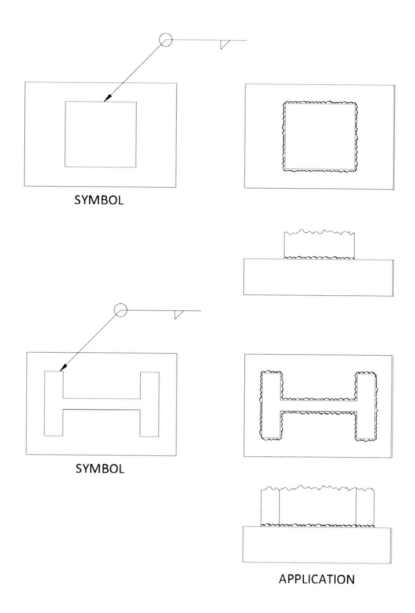

SYMBOL

SYMBOL

APPLICATION

C – Reference line is used to divide the arrow side from the other side of the weld.

D – Field weld symbol is used mostly in the steel construction industry where the welding elements (beams and columns) are very large and if welded in a shop there will be a transportation problem. That is why those huge elements are welded on site which requires a highly experienced welder. Field weld in most cases is very difficult and also dangerous because of height and weather conditions.

225

E- Tail is used as a place where we specify the required welding process that needs to be used.

F – SMAW – shielded metal arc welding process is required to be used.

G – Length of the weld (3")

H – Pitch of welds (5")

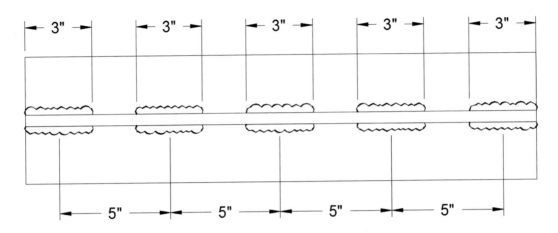

I – (5/16"); Depth of preparation. If the plates are thicker than ¼" then we have to prepare them for welding. Preparation requires to make a grove with a specific depth which is determined by the thickness of the plates.

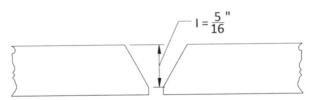

J – (3/8"); Effective throat represents the total depth of the weld which is simply the thickness of the plates to be welded.

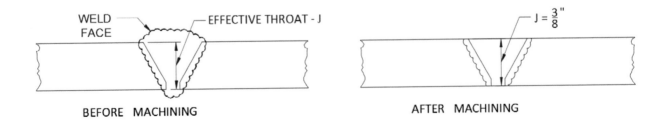

K – In many cases after welding, an additional (finishing) operation is required. Based on the function of the welded parts additional finishing operations could be:

ADDITIONAL (FINISHING) OPERATION	MACHINING	GRINDING	ROLLING	HAMMER
DESIGNATION	M	G	R	H

L – Contour symbol could be:

———————— FLAT　　　　⌣ CONCAVE　　　　⌢ CONVEX

This designates the finished surface of the weld and has to be shaped as the contour symbol requires.

M – grove angle is normally 60° and it is used when we do preparation of the plates by making a groove because the plates are thick. Based on the type of material being welded this grove could be made by using an automatically moving torch, milling or grinding process.

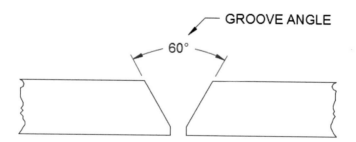

N – Root opening (1/8") is based on the thickness and type of preparation of the plates

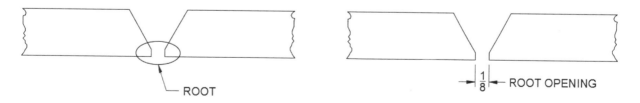

O – V-groove as already explained, is made as preparation of the plates for welding. The groove angle is normally 60° but could be 45° or 30°. Common practice is: Root opening increases as the angle decreases.

227

21.2 Types of Joints and their Preparations

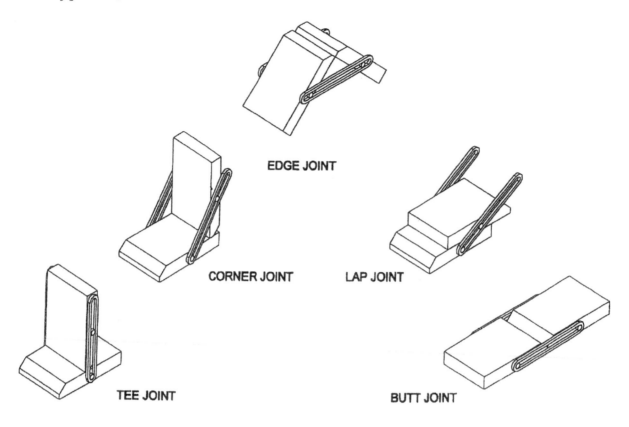

EDGE JOINT

CORNER JOINT

LAP JOINT

TEE JOINT

BUTT JOINT

21.3 Fillet Welds

On the general welding symbol fillet welds are normally shown as a triangular shape although the hypotenuse of the triangle could be flat, concave or convex in shape.

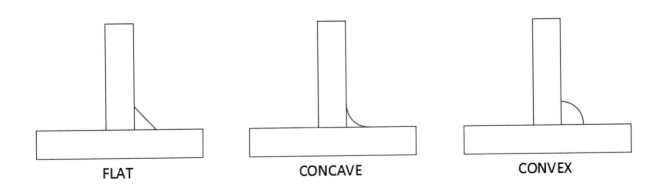

FLAT

CONCAVE

CONVEX

Fillet weld symbol could be shown on arrow side, on the other side or on both sides.

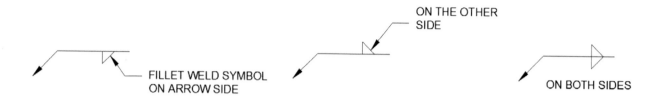

If the fillet welds need to be welded and look flat, concave or convex, then the fillet symbols should look like this (see following image).

In order welded plates to be considered safe to be used, fillet weld has to be strong enough to withstand the forces applied on the plates. For that reason, fillet weld has to be made with specific size(s) shown on the fillet weld symbol.

Generally there are 3 sizes: size 1 (leg 1); size 2 (leg 2);; and effective throughout.

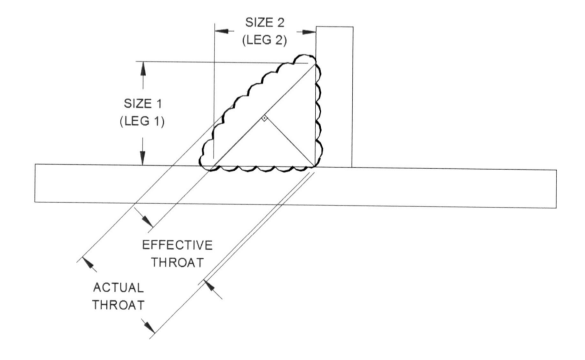

Note: terms Leg 1 and Leg 2 are normally used by welders in shops as a common welders terms.

On welding symbols, normally size 1 and size 2 are shown. They could be shown on one or both sides (arrow and the other side).

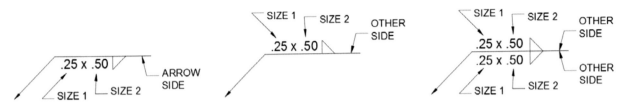

If size 1 is equal to side 2, then we put only one size.

SIZE 1 = SIZE 2 = .25

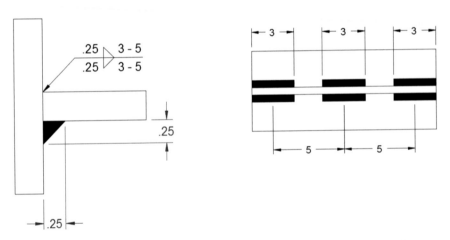

If fillet weld sizes are equal size 1 = size 2 and it is applied across each other on the plates, then the symbol looks like this: see following image

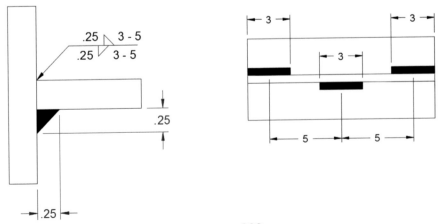

Staggered fillet welds are very common and more practical than the regular (across each other) fillets. Staggered fillet welds are shown in the following image.

Chapter 22

APPENDIXES

Appendix 1:   BASIC LAYERS

Name	Color	Line Type	Line Weight
CENTERLINE	RED	CENTERLINE	0.25
HIDDEN	YELLOW	HIDDEN	0.35
OBJECT	GREEN	CONTINUOUS	0.70
TEXT	BLUE	CONTINUOUS	0.35
DIMENSIONS	MAGENTA	CONTINUOUS	0.25

Appendix 2:   SYMBOLS

%% d – DEGREES (º)

%% p – PLUS/MINUS (±)

%% c – DIAMETER (Ø)

%% u – <u>TEXT UNDERLINED</u>

%% o – T̄EXT OVERLINED

STEPS IN USING SYMBOLS FROM THE CHARACTER MAP

1. On the Command line type **MT** (for MULTIPLE TEXT) and **click ENTER,** or click on the MULTIPLE TEXT button (A) located at the bottom of the DRAW TOOLBAR

2. Click on the screen to specify the first corner and then the opposite corner for the multiple text box

3. Click on the @ symbol

4. Slide the cursor down the Symbol until cascade menu opens, then at the bottom of the menu **select Other**... and the Character Map will open

5. From the Character Map click on the **symbol** you want to use

6. Click **Select** then **Copy**

7. Close the Character Map

8. Click the right mouse button anywhere in the text area

9. Click on **Paste**

Appendix 3:   BREAK LINE – SHORT

1. Place your cursor where you want the break line to begin
2. Command (type it): **SKETCH** and hit **ENTER**
3. Record Increment: **0.1** hit **ENTER**
4. Sketch: **Drag your Cursor to a Specific point**
5. Hit: **ENTER**
6. **TRIM** of the appropriate segments

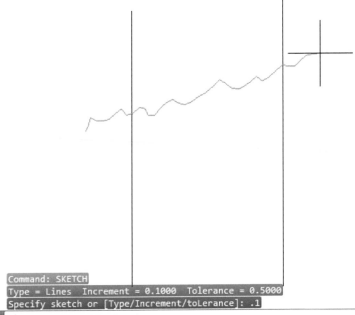

1. Create a **PHANTOM LINE LAYER** (Line type: Select PHANTOM LINE)
2. Click on **POLYLINE Command** to start **AN ARROW**
3. Specify start point: **CLICK** in the position **to Start an ARROW** (Have your **ORTHO ON**)
4. Select and type it: **W** (for **WIDTH**)
5. Hit **ENTER**
6. Specify Starting Width: type **0 and hit ENTER**
7. Specify Ending Width: type **0.2 and hit ENTER**
8. Specify the next point: Select and type it: **L** (for **LENGTH**)
9. Specify the Length of Line: type **0.6 and hit ENTER**

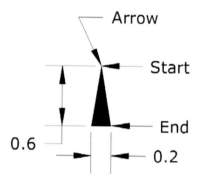

You have just created an ARROW (see above) **as a part of Viewing and Cutting plane Lines**
To continue with VIEWING LINE go to Step 10

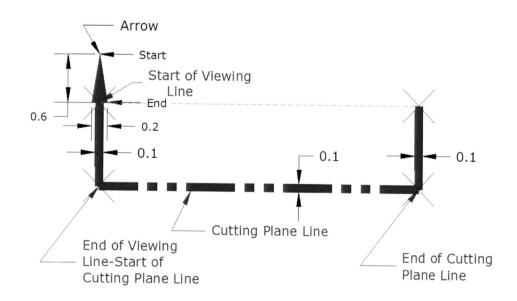

10. Specify next point (…): type **W** and **hit Enter**
11. Specify Starting Width (0.200): type **0.1 and hit ENTER**
12. Specify Ending Width (0.100): **hit ENTER** to accept 0.100
13. Specify the next point: **Click at the End of the Viewing Plane Line** (see image below)
14. Specify next: **Click at the other side (End)** to specify the length of **Cutting Plane Line**
15. Move your cursor up at the **End Point of the first Arrow**
16. Specify next point (…): **type W and hit Enter**
17. Specify Starting Width (0.100): type **0.2 and hit ENTER**
18. Specify Ending Width (0.200): type **0 and hit ENTER**
19. Specify the next point (…): type **L** (for **LENGTH**) and **hit Enter**
20. Specify the Length of Line: type **0.6 and hit ENTER**
21. **Hit Esc** – see complete image below

Appendix 5:   VIEWPORTS in Layout: Assignment 9.5

1. After creating the BRACKET & DETAILS (assignment 10.6) drawing in Model Space,
2. Click the tab that says **Layout 1** (seen in figure 1) to create a layout of the BRACKET & DETAILS drawing.
3. DELETE your drawing in the Layout
4. CREATE a viewport layer
5. CREATE four viewports (Use the FIT function)
6. CREATE four different Dimension Layers (Note: Use a different dimension layer for each individual viewport

Dimension Layer 1 – for viewport 1
Dimension Layer 2 – for viewport 2
Dimension Layer 3 – for viewport 3
Dimension Layer 4 – for viewport 4

Note: If you don't want a specific dimension to be shown in a specific Viewport use the FREEZE IN CURRENT VIEWPORT option (third button in the Layer command – click on the ↓ in the layer command and see Figure 2)

Figure 1.

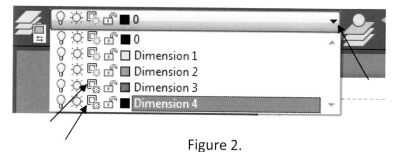

Figure 2.

A) DRAWING UNITS:

1. Click on: **FORMAT**
2. Click on: **Units**
3. TYPE: **Architectural**
4. PRECISION: **0'-01/16"**
5. UNITS: **Inches**

B) DRAWING LIMITS:

1. Specify Lower Left corner type: **0,0** hit **Enter**
2. Specify Upper Right corner type: **200', 200'** hit **Enter**

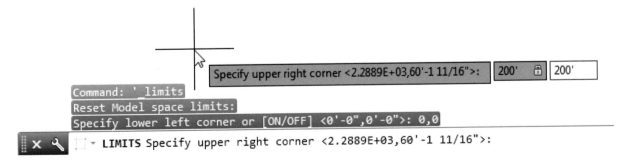

C) ZOOM ALL:

Appendix 7: USING PREVIOUSLY CREATED BLOCKS (For Office Layout Assignment 10.2)

Note: YOU MUST BE ON LAYER 0 WHEN CREATING NEW BLOCKS

1. Following the procedure for MAKING A BLOCK, **make the Furniture BLOCKS** (DESKS, TABLE, DRAFTING BOARD, FILE CABINET, DRAFTING STOOL AND CHAIR using dimensions specified in Fig.1. Use text height 10")

2. Save them as lib1

3. Open a New File (inch system) – Following instructions in Appendix 6

4. Draw the Walls of the Engineering Department room according to the layout shown in Fig. 2 on the Assignment 11.2 – (see next page)

5. Create 8 different Layers, using 8 different colors (6 Layers for the 6 Blocks created in Step 1; Object Layer for the Walls and Dimensioning Layer)

6. Go to the Design Center

7. Click on the Open Drawings

8. Click on the (+) Drawing 1

9. Click on Blocks

10. Drag the Blocks to your drafting area

11. Close the Design Center

12. Place the Blocks according to Fig.2 Engineering department drawing. Note: You will need to Rotate, Move and Align you blocks to get the required Layout.

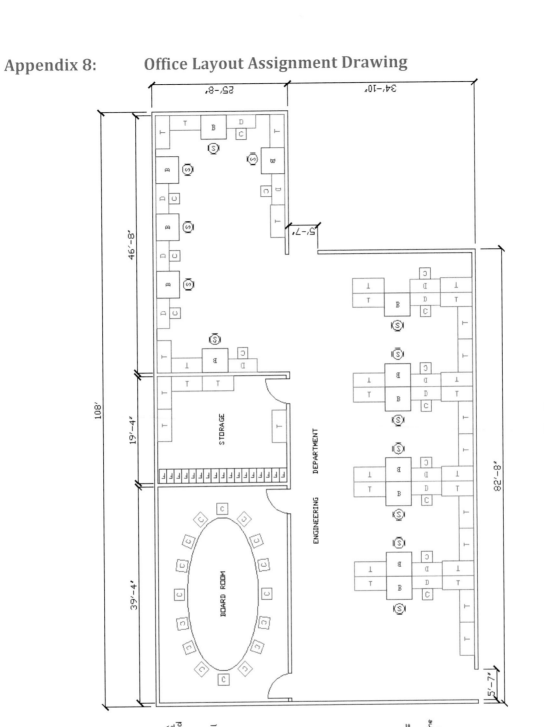

238

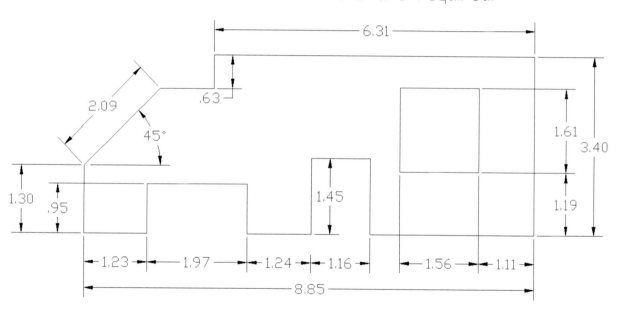

ASSIGNMENT 3.5

Use AutoCAD to draw the metric drawing shown below
Note: No dimensions are required

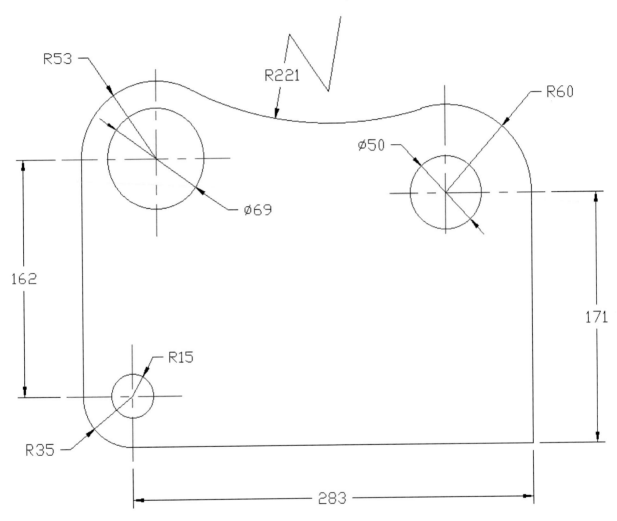

ASSIGNMENT 4.2

Use AutoCAD to draw the drawing shown below
Note: No dimensions are required

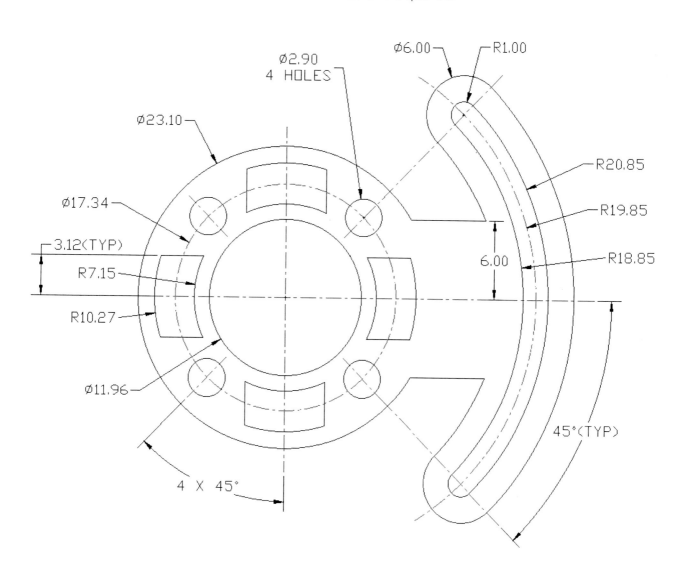

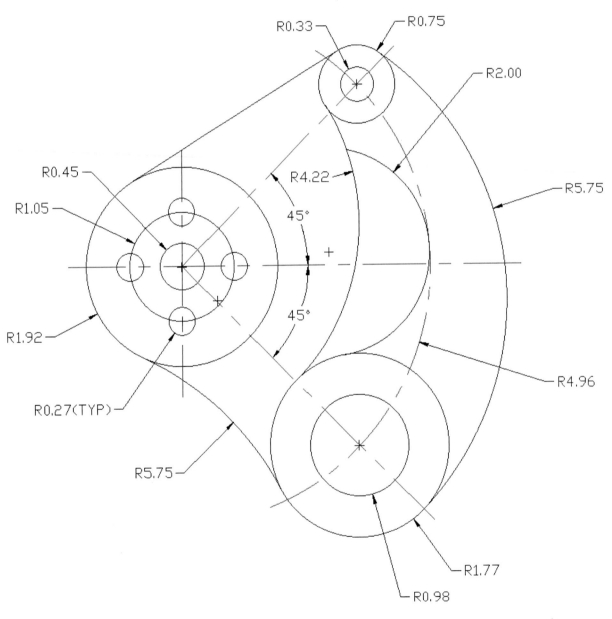

ASSIGNMENT 5.3

Use AutoCAD to draw the drawing shown below
Note: No dimensions are required

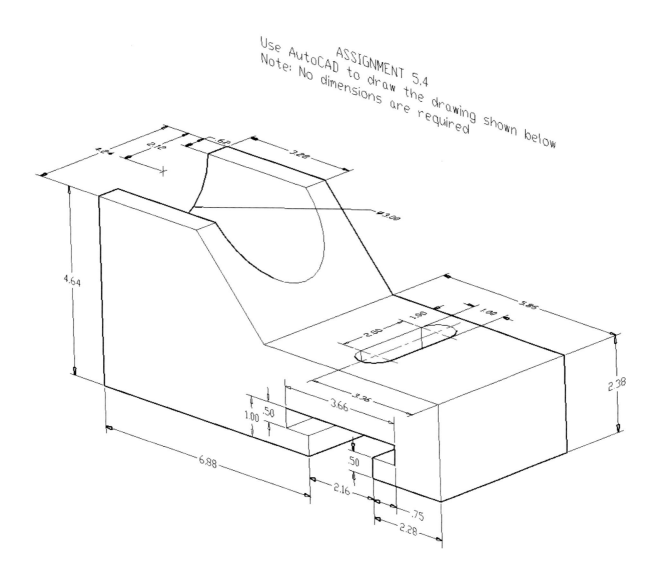

ASSIGNMENT 5.4
Use AutoCAD to draw the drawing shown below
Note: No dimensions are required

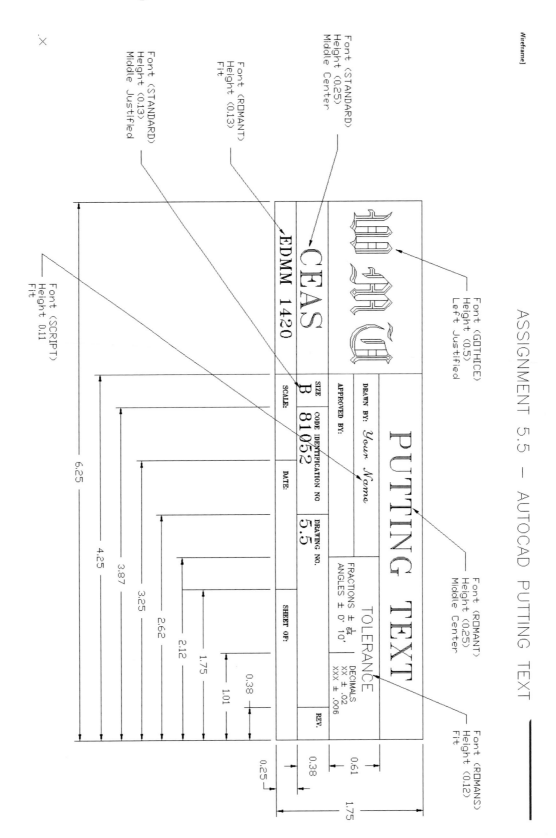

ASSIGNMENT 8.3
Use AutoCAD to draw Full Sectional view of the part shown below

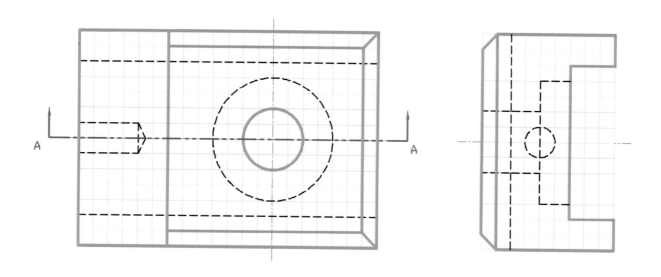

ASSIGNMENT 8.4
Use AutoCAD to draw the drawing with dimensions shown below

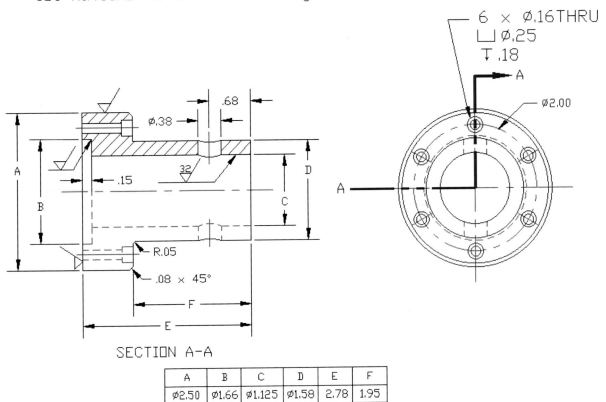

SECTION A-A

A	B	C	D	E	F
Ø2.50	Ø1.66	Ø1.125	Ø1.58	2.78	1.95

PART NAME: CAM SUPPORT
MATERIAL: STEEL
UNLESS OTHERWISE SPECIFIED-
TOLERANCES ON TWO PLACE DIMENSIONS ±.03
TOLERANCES ON THREE PLACE DIMENSIONS ±.001

63 / EXCEPT WHERE NOTED

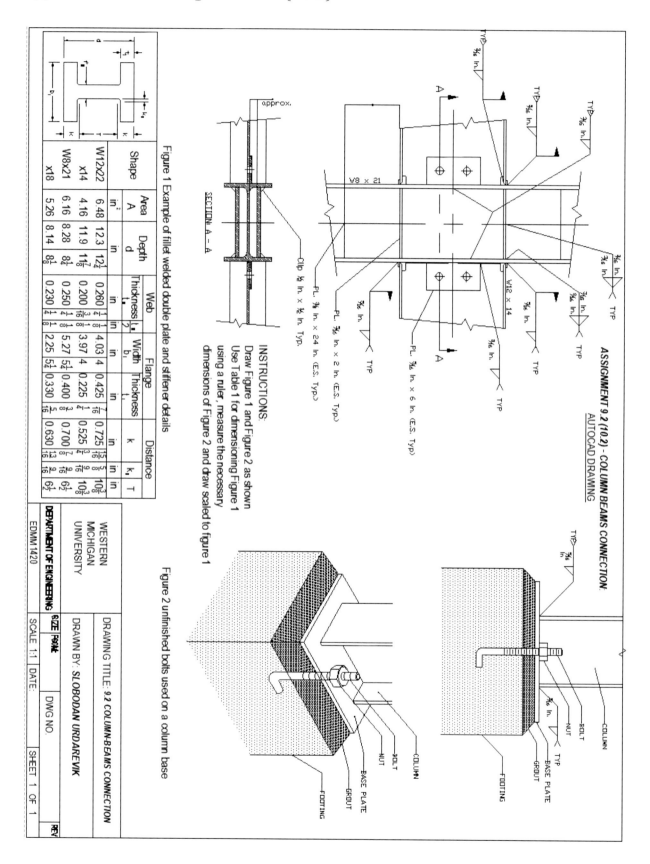

ASSIGNMENT 9.2 (10.2) - COLUMN BEAMS CONNECTION:
AUTOCAD DRAWING

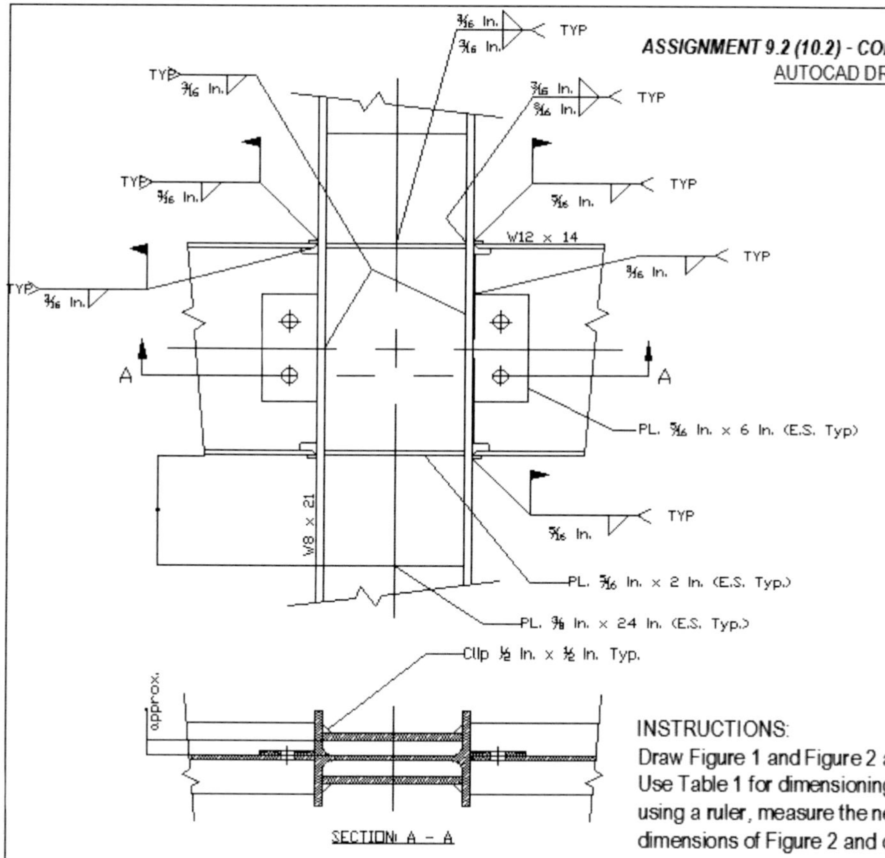

Figure 1 Example of fillet welded double plate and stiffener details

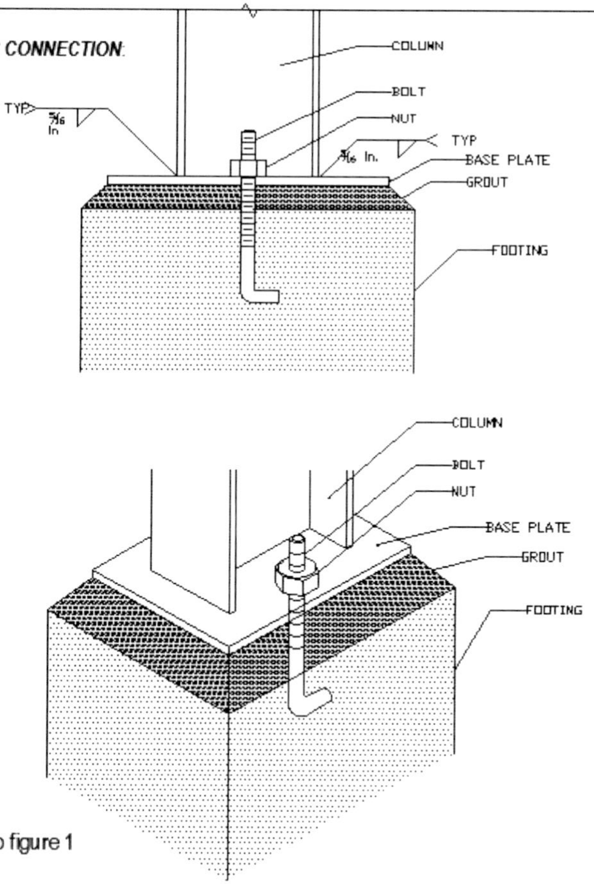

Figure 2 unfinished bolts used on a column base

INSTRUCTIONS:
Draw Figure 1 and Figure 2 as shown
Use Table 1 for dimensioning Figure 1
using a ruler, measure the necessary
dimensions of Figure 2 and draw scaled to figure 1

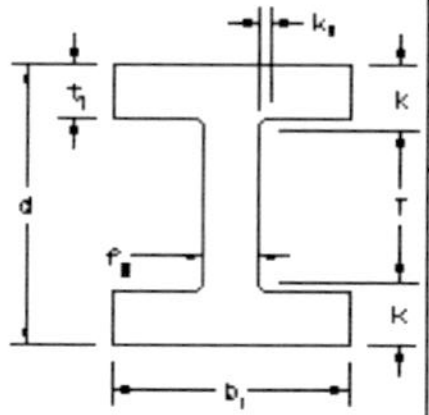

Shape	Area A	Depth d		Web Thickness t_w		$\frac{t_w}{2}$	Flange Width b_f		Flange Thickness t_f		Distance k		k_1	T
	in²	in		in		in	in		in		in		in	in
W12x22	6.48	12.3	$12\frac{1}{4}$	0.260	$\frac{1}{4}$	$\frac{1}{8}$	4.03	4	0.425	$\frac{7}{16}$	0.725	$\frac{15}{16}$	$\frac{5}{8}$	$10\frac{3}{8}$
x14	4.16	11.9	$11\frac{7}{8}$	0.200	$\frac{3}{16}$	$\frac{1}{8}$	3.97	4	0.225	$\frac{1}{4}$	0.525	$\frac{3}{4}$	$\frac{9}{16}$	$10\frac{3}{8}$
W8x21	6.16	8.28	$8\frac{1}{4}$	0.250	$\frac{1}{4}$	$\frac{1}{8}$	5.27	$5\frac{1}{4}$	0.400	$\frac{3}{8}$	0.700	$\frac{7}{8}$	$\frac{9}{16}$	$6\frac{1}{2}$
x18	5.26	8.14	$8\frac{1}{8}$	0.230	$\frac{1}{4}$	$\frac{1}{8}$	2.25	$5\frac{1}{4}$	0.330	$\frac{5}{16}$	0.630	$\frac{13}{16}$	$\frac{9}{16}$	$6\frac{1}{2}$

WESTERN MICHIGAN UNIVERSITY	DRAWING TITLE: ***9.2 COLUMN-BEAMS CONNECTION***		
	DRAWN BY: ***SLOBODAN URDAREVIK***		
DEPARTMENT OF ENGINEERING	SIZE FSCM:	DWG NO.	REV
EDMM 1420	SCALE 1:1	DATE:	SHEET 1 OF 1

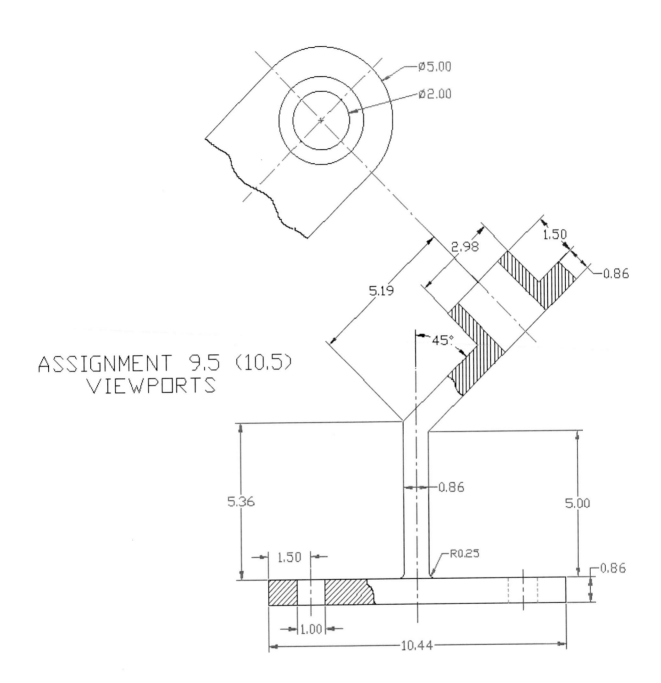

ASSIGNMENT 9.5 (10.5)
VIEWPORTS

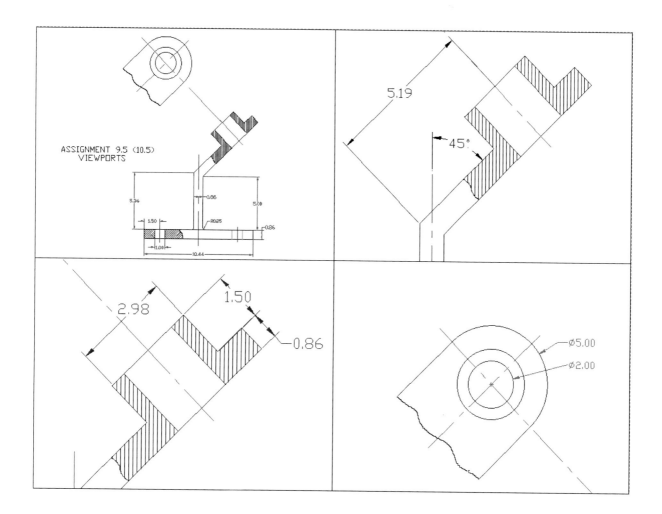

ASSIGNMENT 11.2 (12.2)
3D-Solid model

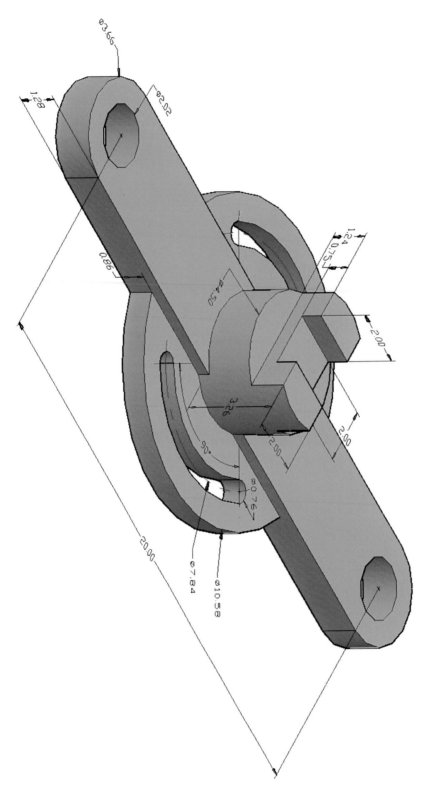

Getting Started

1. To begin, go to Start > All Programs > CAD > Autodesk > Autodesk Inventor 2019 > Autodesk Inventor Professional 2019 - English.

2. When open, close Customer Involvement Program and Welcome bars then click on the 'new' [new icon] button at the top left corner.

    Standard (mm).ipt

    a.   Click on the 'metric' tab and then open the **Standard (mm).ipt**

3. You should be looking at a grey sketch window. Now you can begin the first part.

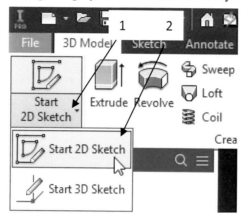

Top Half

1. Click on the small arrow first and then click on 'Start 2D Sketch' button shown above.

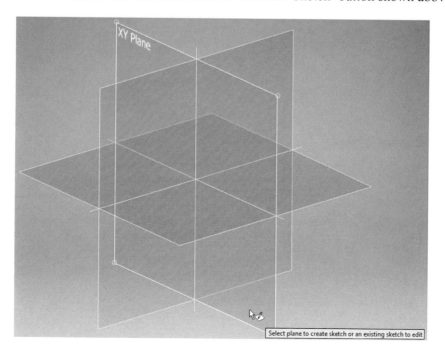

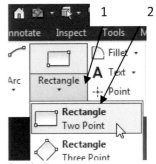

Click on the Horizontal Plane to create the first part.

2. To start creating the geometry we need, click on the **Rectangle** button.

    a. Create a rectangle of any size in the display area.

    b. Now it's time to define the rectangle's size. Click on the dimension button.

        i. Click on one of the lines to select the rectangle's length and width to dimension.

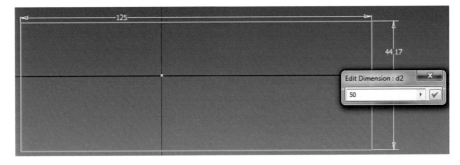

Dimension

        ii. When you have the dimensions created, double click on the actual numbers of the dimension and redefine the correct sizes. **Length = 125mm. Width = 50mm.**

3. Next, we need to extrude this geometry. Click on Finish Sketch to switch to 3D modeling.

    a. Hit F6. This will bring you to a SE isometric view. Next, select the extrude button. A window will appear that asks you for a height and asks you to select the profile to extrude. Since we only have one profile, it is already selected. Enter **40** for the height and click OK.

Extrude

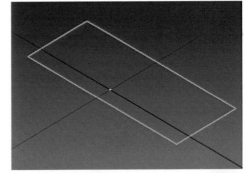

    b. To rotate this geometry click on the **Orbit** button on the right side of the model space. This command works very much the same as 'orbit' in AutoCAD. Remember, you can always return to SE isometric by clicking F6.

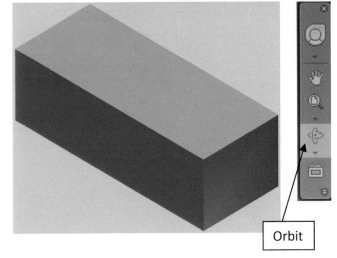

Orbit

4. Now we need to create the holes in this part. We will be using the **Extrude** command again, but first we must define where these holes are to be located.

   a. First, click on the **Start 2D Sketch** button on the top left navigation toolbar. Then, click the top surface of the box to create a sketch plane on that surface.

   Start 2D Sketch

   Sketch

   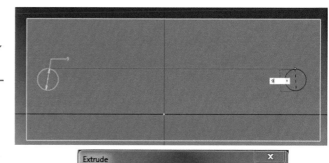

   b. Create two circles near the ends of the geometry by clicking on the **Circle** command.

   Circle

   c. Click on the **Dimension** button to define the size of the circles (**Ø9mm**), and their placement from the sides of the geometry. They should be 25mm from the sides and 10mm from the ends.

   Dimension

   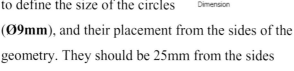

   d. Once done, click on the Model tab again and select the **Extrude** command. Select both the circle's profiles, click on the Boolean cut option, then select the distance (it should go through the part). Click OK.

   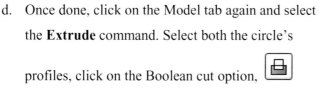

   e. Do the same procedure to create the large half circle (Ø55mm) thru the part.

5. Finally, we will round the edges of the part.

   a. Click on the **Fillet** command and select the size to be 4mm. Then, select all four edges that need to be filleted. Click OK.

   Fillet

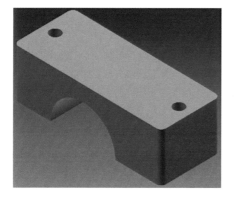

Click Here
To Save

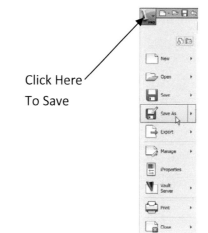

6. Save the part as 'Top Half'.

Lower Half

1. To begin the lower half, we must begin a new part. Click on the 'new' 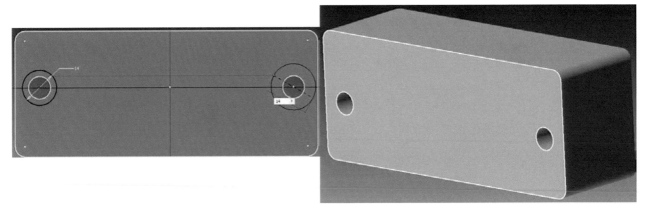 button. Select the metric tab and select **Standard(mm).ipt**
2. To begin creating the lower half, follow the same procedure as creating the top half One obvious difference is that you must create the other side of the semicircle cut through the part.
3. To create the counter bore hole at the bottom of the part, we will first create a sketch on the bottom of the part using the **Start 2D Sketch** command.

   Start
   2D Sketch
   Sketch

   a. Create two Ø14 circles centered on the existing Ø9 holes.

4. **Extrude** the two circles for 8mm. Use the Boolean operation 'cut' to cut the counter bore into the part.

5. Save the part as 'Lower Half'

Strap

1. To begin the strap, we must begin a new part. Click on the 'new' 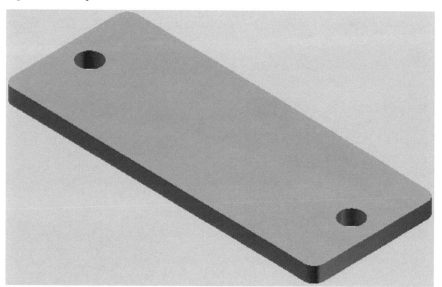 button. Select the metric tab and select **Standard (mm).ipt**

2. Create the strap using the same procedure and commands as the other two parts, paying careful attention to sizing and making sure to create the fillets. Extrude the strap 6mm.

3. Save the part as 'Strap'

Hex Bolt

1. To begin the hex bolt, we must begin a new part. Click on the 'new' button. Select the metric tab and select **Standard (mm).ipt**

Overall Dimensions for the Hex Bolt

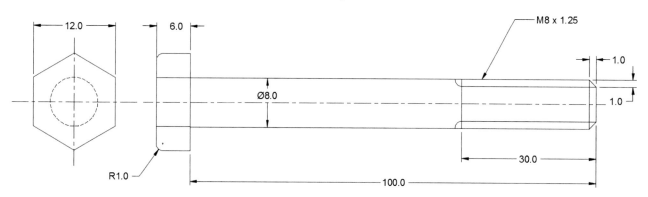

2. In the sketch, create a hexagon using the **Polygon** command.

    a. Define the width using the **Dimension** button across flats to be 12mm.

    b. **Extrude** this to a height of 6mm.

    c. Once extruded, round all the top edges using the **Fillet** command with a radius of 1mm. Note: selecting "loop" will allow you to fillet all 6 edges at once.

3. On the bottom surface of this extrusion, create a **Sketch**.

    a. Draw a circle centered in the middle of the hexagon and define it to have a diameter of 8mm. you might have to dimension it carefully to make sure it is centered on the hexagon.

    b. **Extrude** this circle below the hexagon to a distance of 100mm.

4. To create the thread, click the **Thread** command. 🗒 Thread

    a. Uncheck on the box labeled 'Full Length'. Change the length to be 30mm.

    b. Click on the face button, and click somewhere on the bottom half of the cylinder (so the threads appear on the bottom of the cylinder).

    c. The thread specification should already be M8x1.25. Click OK.

5. Once threaded, use the **Chamfer** ✐ Chamfer command to make a 1mm x 1mm chamfer around the bottom edge of the cylinder.

6. Save the part as 'Hex Bolt'

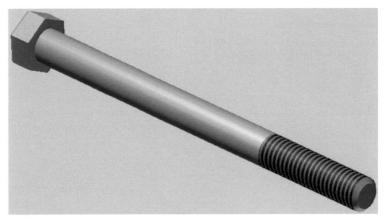

Assembly

1. To begin the assembly, we must begin with a new assembly drawing. Click on the 'new' button. Select the metric tab and select **Standard (mm).iam**

Standard (mm).iam

2. To begin we must get all needed parts into the drawing. Click the **Place** button and find the files labeled 'Top Half', 'Lower Half', 'Strap', and 'Hex bolt'. Place these into the drawing one by one. Place the 'Hex bolt' in twice.

3. Next we need to assemble the parts. Click on the **Constrain** command

Constrain

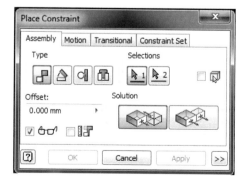

   a. In the constraint window that will appear, click on the insert type of constraint.

b. To use this, click on the top surface of the bottom half (with the arrow pointed up) and the bottom surface of the top half (with the arrow pointed down). Be sure to click **apply** to complete the function. This will join the top and bottom half.

c. Proceed by placing the strap on the top of the 'top half' and the bolts through the holes as shown. Be sure to pay careful attention to the order in which you are selecting the parts and the location of the red circle that appears on the part. For example, the red circle on the bolt should be located at the top of the cylinder as shown.

d. Once completed, the assembly should not be able to be pulled apart by clicking and dragging.

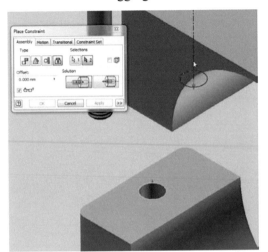
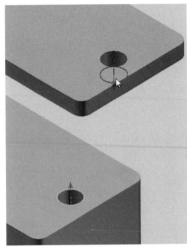

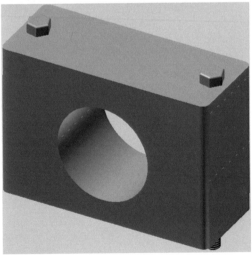

Instructions for Turning in the Assignment

1. Be sure to include all four (4) **Standard (mm).ipt** files, which include the top and lower half, hex bolt and the strap. Send your assembly drawing (**Standard (mm).iam**) as well. Without all of these files, your Instructor will not be able to view or grade your assignment.

Appendix 21   AutoCAD 2019 Download Instructions

1. Use the following link to get started.

http://www.autodesk.com/education/free-software/autocad

2. Once you have come to the page shown below click "CREATE ACCOUNT"

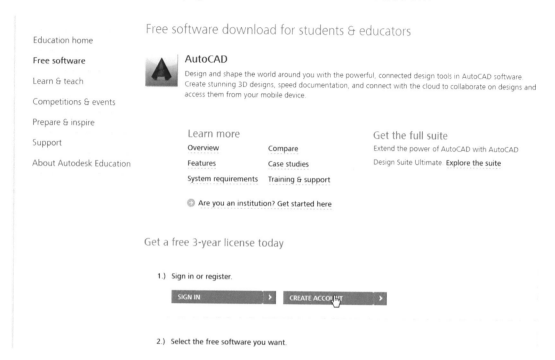

3. You will see this window on your screen, fill out all relevant information and click Next. Note: you must use your Western email that ends in ".edu" to download a student version of the software. Write this information down and keep it for future use (you will also need it in step 6).

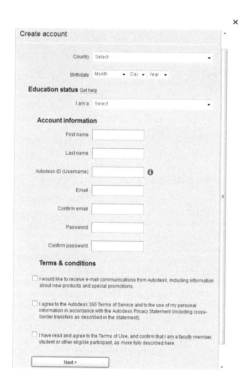

4. An e-mail will be sent to your Western e-mail address which you used in the previous step. Open the e-mail and click on the link to continue installation. You will be brought back to a page shown in the following image. You must click "SIGN IN" at the top of the page.

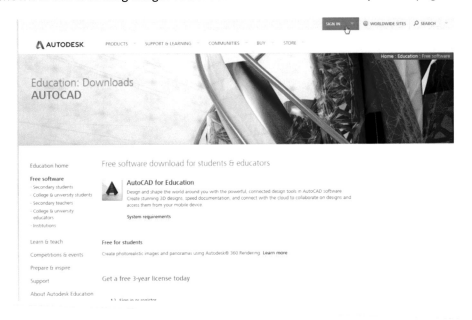

5. Click "SIGN IN" again as shown below.

6. Sign in using the information you provided in step 3. You will be brought to this window shown in the following image. From the drop down menu select version: AutoCAD 2019 Language: English and either a 32 or 64 bit operating system (newer computers are most likely 64 bit). Record the serial number and product key shown on your screen, you will need it to activate your AutoCAD license. Note: 123-12345678 and 123A1 will not work as shown in the following image.

AUTOCAD

AutoCAD

Design and shape the world around you with the powerful, connected design tools in AutoCAD software. Create stunning 3D designs, speed documentation, and connect with the cloud to collaborate on designs and access them from your mobile device.

System Requirements

Welcome back,　　　　Sign out　　My account

AutoCAD 2019 ▼	✓
Windows 64-bit ▼	✓
English ▼	✓

Serial number: **123-12345678**

Product key: **123A1**

Files size: 4.87 GB

Authorized usage: Install on up to 2 personal devices

An email containing the license information above has been sent to you.

+ You are receiving an Educational license　See more

+ Installation restrictions apply　See more

INSTALL NOW ⌄

RECOMMENDED SOFTWARE

 Fusion 360: 3D CAD built for the Cloud
Push, pull and drag designs into the perfect shape with a single cloud-based platform.

- Integrated: Design, test and fabricate
- Connected: Built-in team collaboration
- Accessible: Mac or PC, online or off

CONTINUE >

7. Click "INSTALL NOW" An .exe or execution file will download, if it doesn't automatically appear you may have to go to the downloads folder on your computer to find it, or simply click on the arrow shown in the image below on the top right side of your screen.

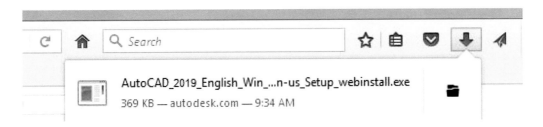

AutoCAD is a very large program and will take a while (possibly 1 hour) to download if your connection is slow. It is best to use the fastest internet connection you can find and to download off peak hours (such as early in the morning).

8. The following image will appear, select "Install on this computer." Another window will appear and you will have to select install again. Now that you have installed the installation installer, AutoCAD will begin to install.

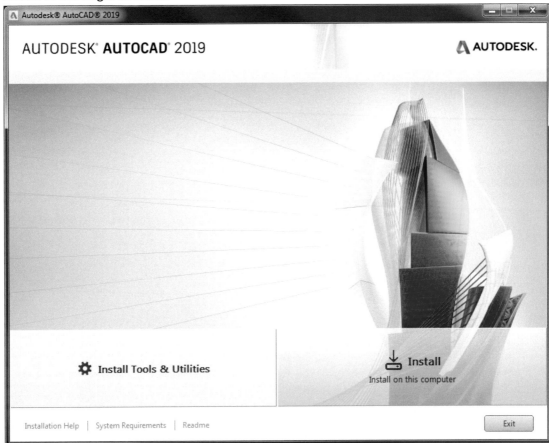

1. Type: "CUI" into the command line and hit Enter. CUI stands for customize user interface.
2. Right click on workspaces and select "New Workspace"
   Name your new workspace "AutoCAD Classic"
3. Right click on AutoCAD Classic and select "set current"
4. Open drop down Toolbars Icon, find Draw and Modify. Individually click and drag these to the Toolbars label in the "Workspace Contents" window on the top right side of the screen as shown in the following image.

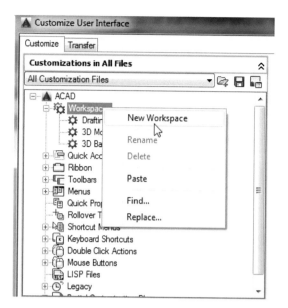

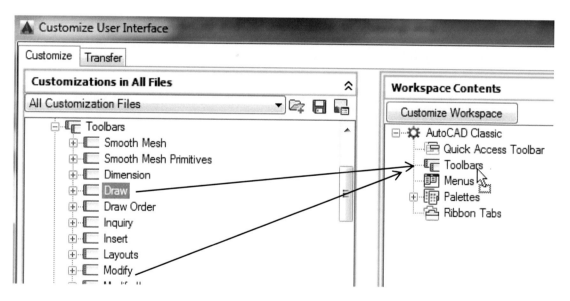

Creating Menu Bar

5. Repeat steps in the CUI as before, this time we will work with "Menu"
6. Select "AutoCAD Classic" and make sure it is highlighted, it is easy to select a menu and loose the workspace contents window and the properties of that menu will be displayed in its place. If you lose the workspace contents window on the top right remember, select "AutoCAD Classic" that you created earlier.
7. Individually click and drag all Menus from "File" to "Help" into the "Menu" portion on the right side as shown before with the toolbars. Note: These must be done individually.

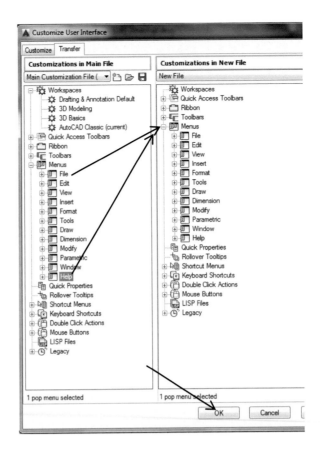

8. Right click on the Ribbon at top of screen, select "Undock" and close the ribbon.

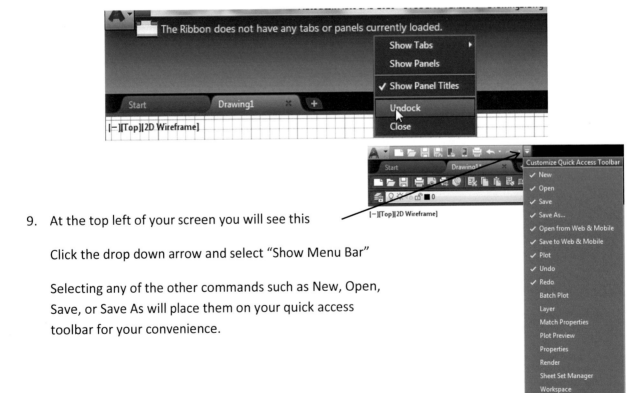

9. At the top left of your screen you will see this

   Click the drop down arrow and select "Show Menu Bar"

   Selecting any of the other commands such as New, Open, Save, or Save As will place them on your quick access toolbar for your convenience.